# the MANual

## the complete man's
## guide to life

Thorsons
*An Imprint of* HarperCollins*Publishers*

Thorsons
An Imprint of HarperCollins*Publishers*
77–85 Fulham Palace Road
Hammersmith, London W6 8JB
1160 Battery Street
San Francisco, California 94111–1213

Published by Thorsons 1996
10 9 8 7 6 5 4 3 2 1

Mick Cooper and Peter Baker assert the moral right to
be identified as the authors of this work

A catalogue record for this book
is available from the British Library

ISBN 0 7225 3318 7

Printed in Great Britain by
Caledonian International Book Manufacturing Ltd, Glasgow

# contents

**dedication**

to John, Marc and Neil
– for their humour, humanity and hummus.

# acknowledgements

We would like to give special thanks to: Mandy Little for her persistence and encouragement; Kitty and Charles Cooper for their time, support and envelope-licking skills; Elsie Owusu for putting up with us; Grace Lau for her wonderful photos; and Eric Litznaitsky, Graham Saggars and John Jordan for their effort and encouragement. Peter would like to thank Jo Harris for her love, commitment, support, wisdom and wonderful sense of fun; Ida and Lewis Baker for planting the seed that made it all happen; and Helen Baker for providing much-needed sanctuary. Mick would like to thank Helen Cruthers for her love, patience, critical eye and honesty; Colleen Passard for her wisdom, warmth and playfulness; and James Sanderson for being the best mate in the world.

Thanks also to everyone who read through drafts of the chapters and gave us their comments: Neil Blacklock, Chris Cherry, Tom Cooper, Howie Cruthers, Phillip Edwards, Anna Ferguson, Edward Hayes, Tim Kahn, Pete Jenkins, Richard Lang, William Larsden, Alan Lawrie, Bernd Leygraff, Rae McGowan, Richard Myers, Tom O'Brien, John Rowan, Andrew

Samuels, John Wadmore, Nigel Williams, Nick Winslow, Paul Wolf-Light and Gavin Yamey. Thanks, too, to everyone who helped with our research and took part in the discussions and interviews we held. Needless to say, the contents of the book are the responsibility of the authors alone.

# foreword

If men as a sex were quoted on the stock exchange, nobody would buy the shares. At every level of education, men are increasingly out-performed by women. Men lack the cooperative, intuitive skills required in the future teamworking world. We are more prone to stress and illness in everyday life. The male suicide rate has increased by 70 per cent over the past 10 years but the female suicide rate is actually falling. We achieve significantly shorter life spans.

Women find us inadequate in close relationships, divorcing men twice as often as men divorce women. As a result of masculine prejudice, men are failing to ask for help. While women enjoy a universe of outside support, men don't even have each other. On all available evidence, we face a gender crisis for the foreseeable future. In every sense of the word, *modern men don't work*.

Our reactions so far have been both myopic and depressing. We've seen a short-lived gesture towards domestication ('new man'), a risible exercise in 'going native' ('iron man'), and a pathetic attempt to ask women to stop hitting men where it hurts ('whining man').

That's why I'm especially glad to endorse this book by Mick Cooper and Peter Baker. Rather than push some minority line, pet theme or new chauvinist solution, it tackles men as a whole and as we are. I said in my book, *Men: An Investigation Into The Emotional Male* (BBC Books, 1984), that men must use the media to help themselves change. When, in 1983, I asked an assistant in a bookshop to direct me to the shelves of books about men, she looked as startled as if I'd asked about Martians. She wouldn't be so surprised today. Men are finally breaking their silence and *The MANual* offers genuine words of help for all of us.

Ever since the industrial revolution, men have elected to become alienated from much domestic experience and deprived of contact with their children. Now society is electing to terminate many paid masculine jobs. Over 80 per cent of new jobs will go to women. Only by reaffirming their relevance at home and in the family, by finding an identity through 'being' not 'doing', will men become civilized again. *The MANual* is a first-class guide.

Phillip Hodson, February 1996

# preface

There's been a lot of talk about men recently: 'new men', 'wild men', 'new lads', 'wild lads', 'post new-men', even 'new post-men' (well almost) ... The list goes on and on. It gets confusing; and it doesn't seem to have got anyone very far. Which is where *The MANual* comes in. This book puts together in a practical and down-to-earth format the central issues facing men in the 90s. Its central theme concerns the social and psychological pressures many of us still feel to be 'real men'; how these can limit our lives; and the paths along which we can discover many new, different and enjoyable ways of being men.

If we compare men's lives to a game of soccer, it seems that many of us are like players who have learnt to kick the ball with only one foot and in only one direction. This doesn't allow much opportunity for creative play, let alone goal scoring. We'd obviously stand much more chance of success if we could play flexibly, using both feet (and maybe our heads too) and passing the ball wherever we like. This book is a kind of training manual for us to improve our skills – not for soccer but for life. It isn't a guide to becoming the perfect man; it's about how we can open up those aspects of ourselves we too often hide, combining the best of the qualities traditionally associated with being male and female. In this way, we can become sensitive *as well as* strong, gentle *as well as* assertive, intimate *as well as* independent. It's about how we can become '*complete* men'.

The book starts with a look at the characteristics of the traditional real man – that tough, powerful but cool individual who copes with any crisis, makes love to any woman and, ultimately, conquers all his foes. He's Arnold Schwarzenegger, Clint Eastwood, Richard Gere, James Bond, Richard Branson and Captain Kirk all rolled into one – an absurd image, perhaps, but still one with a tight grip on the male psyche. We will search for his origins in the primaeval swamps and caves and explain how he has been able to survive for so long, despite now being well past his sell-by date.

*The MANual* then explores seven key aspects of men's lives: emotions, relationships, sex, violence, health, work and fatherhood. In each of these areas, it examines how our struggle to live up to the ideal of the real man has affected and constrained us. The book suggests how we can begin to take a fresh look at ourselves, as well as the people around us. In any situation, a man doesn't have to be satisfied with the automatic knee-jerk response of the real man – or, in computer-speak, his 'default' programme. Instead, he can learn to ask himself, 'What *choices* do I have here?' or 'What's the most appropriate response?' In other words, a man doesn't have to do what a man's gotta do, but can decide to do what he thinks and feels is right for him. This apparently simple step, as we shall see, opens up a vast number of exciting, challenging and, at times, frightening possibilities.

As we approach the millennium, there are many good reasons for re-evaluating our lives. Whether we like it or not, men are being profoundly affected by a world undergoing rapid, and sometimes unsettling, change. The economy is shifting fundamentally, as heavy industry gives way to service industry and secure employment is replaced with temporary contracts. Relationships, including marriages, are becoming increasingly unstable and short-lived. The emergence of HIV and AIDS has obliged many of us, whether we're straight or gay, to rethink and change our sexual behaviour. Crucially, too, women are becoming more powerful, asserting their independence and demanding much more from their relationships with men. Many traditional certainties about, and attitudes towards, gender roles are being challenged and undermined.

Against this background, it's not surprising to find increasing numbers of men (and women) recognizing that traditional ways of being are quickly becoming redundant – perhaps even downright dangerous – and seeking new ways of individual and social transformation. More and more people are now realizing that they can't have satisfying and fulfilling lives unless they develop a greater sense of self-awareness and an understanding of the potential for personal change. *The MANual* suggests ways in which men can seize the opportunity to become part of this dynamic process.

As this book makes clear, however, we can do all this without becoming self-obsessed or taking ourselves too seriously. We may well need to free ourselves from the psychological grip of the stereotyped square-jawed, stiff upper-lipped male hero, but we certainly don't want to model ourselves instead on the sandal-wearing, brown rice-eating new man, who spends hours earnestly discussing his favourite recycling centre or how much fun it is to change a nappy. We need to retain the ability to laugh – especially at ourselves.

While this book tries to be relevant to all men, it's primarily about and for heterosexual men. Although it's vital that gay men are not ignored or side-lined, as authors who both identify as straight, we felt it would have been arrogant and patronizing for us to attempt to write in detail about gay men's issues. We hope, however, that any gay man reading this book will be heartened by our belief that straight men can benefit from reflecting on, and hopefully changing, any traditional feelings they may have about sexuality and sexual orientation. Other groups of men – including black men, older men and disabled men – may also feel that some of their specific issues have not been addressed, but we hope that they will still find much that is relevant and illuminating.

# introduction:
# the real man

## paul

Paul loves making love to Christine – or does he? Both Paul and Christine are teachers in their late 20s and they've been going out together for a couple of months. Paul is strongly attracted to Christine – he says she's the sexiest woman he's ever been to bed with – but although he loves touching her and being touched by her, there are things about their sex life that don't feel quite right:

Soon after we started sleeping together, I began to notice that my mind was wandering while we were making love. I began to worry about how well I was doing as a lover and whether she was really enjoying herself. I became more and more obsessed with the idea that if I didn't do a good enough job in bed, Christine would lose interest in me and find another partner. I know all this anxiety about performance is stupid, but I can't seem to make love any other way.

1

It's got to the point now where Paul's approach is virtually lovemaking by numbers:

> I usually start off by kissing her for a few minutes. Then I think it's time to start moving down her body. Once I've 'done' the breasts, I'll move on to touching her clitoris, either with my hand or my tongue. After a bit of that, I reckon it's time to reach for the condoms.

But Paul's problems are not over once he's inside his partner. In fact, his struggle to be the perfect lover becomes even more intense. Desperate not to come before Christine, he plays mind-games to stop himself ejaculating:

> I read in a sex manual that doing mental arithmetic can help. I usually concentrate on multiplication tables, but when I feel they're not enough, I try to remember bus routes or even who took the penalties at the end of the 1994 World Cup Final.

Once Christine has come, Paul feels he'd better hurry his orgasm along:

> I get worried that if I take too long, she'll think I don't find her attractive. But if I end up worrying about that, I start getting tense and it takes me even longer to come. I sometimes get scared I might lose my erection completely, so then I start imagining Christine in some

crotchless panties, or Sharon Stone crossing her legs in
*Basic Instinct.*

It's only after his orgasm that Paul feels he can finally relax and
really enjoy cuddles and intimacy with Christine.

# jimmy

Jimmy, a 24-year-old computer programmer, likes his beer.
Unfortunately, he sometimes likes it too much and over-
indulges. This happened last Christmas:

> I knew I'd drunk way over my limit. I'd had a couple of bad
> hangovers and had even thrown up, which is quite unusual
> for me. A couple of days later, when I met my friend Max
> in a bar, I was still feeling rather fragile. In fact, I'd decided
> to lay off the booze for a month or two.

As he neared the bar to buy the first round, Jimmy wondered
what to have. Holding up his money to attract the barman's
attention, he eyed up the bottles of alcohol-free lager in the
fridge:

> Not only did I think that the non-alcoholic stuff tastes like
> piss, I felt incredibly embarrassed about just looking at it,
> let alone ordering it. I was worried what the barman
> would think of me and I was even more worried what the
> other blokes standing at the bar would think. After all,    **3**

they were knocking back the beers and they'd be bound to reckon that I was a bit of a wimp.

The barman eventually came over and Jimmy ordered a strong lager for Max. As he watched the glass being filled, he felt more and more uncomfortable at the thought of ordering something non-alcoholic:

I wondered how I could get what I wanted without looking like a dork. I thought about saying that my drink was for Max, who was playing the pinball machine at the other end of the bar. I even considered running out the door. In the end I cracked and asked for another bottle of the strong lager.

## graham

It was a Friday evening and Graham, a manager in his mid-30s, was in a club with his partner Cathy. They bumped into another woman, Jane, who'd been a friend of his for years, although there'd never been anything physical between them. Jane joined them, despite the fact that Cathy obviously wasn't happy about it, and they ended up arguing about Jane on the way home:

I thought Cathy was being unreasonable, and by the time we'd got back to the flat, I was fed up with talking and went straight to bed. When Cathy came up, she turned her back on me and was obviously very annoyed. She started crying and tossing and turning. I had to be up early for work the next day and it felt like she was deliberately trying to keep me awake. Then she started turning on the stereo with the remote control and pulling the covers to her side of the bed. I was getting more and more wound up, and after we'd pulled the covers back and forth for a few minutes, I just rolled on top of her and began punching her in the back and side. I must have hit her three or four times, hard enough to bruise. Then I pinned her down to the bed and told her never, ever to do that again.

This wasn't the last time something like this happened:

After that, there was a pretty regular cycle of violence. Although I was never as violent as I was in that first incident, I would still push her down on the bed, try to intimidate her or shout at her and call her names. It always happened when we were arguing. I'd get incredibly frustrated and reach the stage where it felt as though there was nothing else I could do to get my point across. I suppose I was trying to control her.

About a year later, after another incident, Cathy stormed out of the house. This time she didn't come back – she'd gone straight to a refuge for battered women.

# three men

Paul's, Jimmy's and Graham's stories are different in many ways, but they're linked by a common theme. Each of these men were struggling to live up to the image of the real man. Paul wanted to prove he knows what's what between the sheets; Jimmy tried to show he was 'man enough' to take his beer; and, as for Graham, his violence was a way of showing he was in control.

However, there is something else these men share. The lives of all three were in different ways damaged by their attempts to be real men. If Paul's honest about what goes on when he has sex with his partner, he knows he doesn't actually like it that much. Instead of simply enjoying a good session in the sack, he's far too uptight and worried about his performance to relax and let himself go. Jimmy's anxieties about not appearing a wimp in front of the men around the bar led him to buy – and drink – something he didn't want and which he knew wasn't good for him. Graham not only failed to control his partner but, ultimately, his behaviour also meant he lost her forever.

What's more, in two of these stories, the lives of women were also affected by the real-man syndrome. In the case of Graham's partner, Cathy, this is quite clear: she was brutally assaulted. It's likely, however, that Christine, Paul's partner, also suffers from his efforts to be the perfect lover. While he's wondering about the correct time to tweak her nipples or calculating 12 times 17, she probably feels as if she's making love with a robot.

# searching for the real man

But who or what exactly is the real man? What are the images and ideas in our head that tell us how we, and other men, should be? At first sight, the answer might seem obvious. Yet, as with many definitions, it can prove more elusive on more detailed examination. Would we qualify as a real man if we had bulging biceps like Sylvester Stallone or Chuck Norris? Modelling ourselves on mild-mannered reporter Clark Kent probably wouldn't push us very far up the real-man league table, but what about Superman? Not only does he have phenomenal physical powers, he also, after all, believes in truth and justice and always wears his underpants on the outside.

Would becoming a political leader like Bill Clinton make us a real man because of the massive political and military power at our fingertips, or would we be fatally compromised if, like him, we had a powerful wife? Could we claim real-man status if we possessed the massive intellect of scientist and writer Professor Stephen Hawking, or would being severely disabled rule us out? And what if we were the next Rudolf Nureyev? How would our superb physique and athleticism balance against the fact that we were not just a dancer but a ballet dancer?

Perhaps the core characteristic of the real man is that he's *in control*. When Rambo decides he's going to rescue American prisoners in Vietnam, he doesn't faff around asking permission or filling in paperwork. And he certainly doesn't let the massed ranks of the Vietnamese army stop him either. Through his physical strength and aggression, he gets the job done. A man like Mike Tyson does much the same in the boxing ring: big, muscular and intimidating, he can flatten most of those who dare step inside the ropes to challenge him.

Physical strength is not the only means of exercising power, however. The financial strength of Virgin tycoon Richard Branson pushes him towards the top of the real-man super league. Despite his hippy-like appearance, through his business empire he can virtually hire and fire at will, extending his power over the lives of thousands. And even though John Major may be more of a wimp than Margaret Thatcher, imagine how much more feeble he'd seem if he hadn't become the most powerful political figure in the UK.

As well as having control over others, real men must also control themselves. Mike Tyson doesn't break down and cry when he's knocked out an opponent and neither does John Major after he's half-destroyed the UK economy. A real man must keep a tight rein on his feelings, pretending to the world (as well as to himself) that he's on top of everything. He thinks logically and rationally and doesn't get carried away by his emotions. More expressive men like Woody Allen are seen as wimp-like because they're more ready to reveal their fears, anxieties and sense of inadequacy.

To be in charge, a man also has to be *active*. Clearly, this involves more than sitting around thinking. That's why a man like Stephen Hawking can be recognized as a genius but still fail to make the grade as a real man. Just compare him to John Wayne on his ranch. Every day Wayne's out looking after his cattle and, when someone tries to steal them, he goes

searching for the cattle rustlers as well. He doesn't sit back in his rocking chair and ask his wife to do it. A real man always has to be ready to act. If he sees a car overheating on the hard shoulder, he's ready with the monkey wrench to help out the damsel in distress. And even if he doesn't know how to fix cars, as long as he can just bang the bonnet he can save face. It doesn't matter too much what he does, so long as he's doing something.

What's more, if a man wants to be in control, he must be *independent*. He shouldn't be living at home with his parents when he's 40, nor can he be tied down by his wife and 2.4 kids in a little house in the suburbs. The real man is free and easy, with no strings attached. He sleeps under the stars at night and roams the motorways by day. Nobody tells him what to do – no boss, no dependants, no government. In his Spaghetti Westerns, Clint Eastwood was the ultimate symbol of male independence – he was so free, he had neither a past nor even a name.

Being dominant also means that a real man has the capacity to *protect* others. In fact, it's almost his duty to do so. Take the story of *The Magnificent Seven*. At first, Yul Brynner and his gang of gunfighters simply hoped to make some money by protecting a Mexican community from marauding bandits. But they ended up providing their services for free when they witnessed the terrible suffering of the peasants. No real man could let those around him, particularly his own family, be exploited or destroyed. Instead, he uses his physical strength or, in some cases, his financial power, to protect the weak and the defenceless.

He can do all this because he's also *fearless*. The real man isn't afraid of working on a building site without a hard hat, walking through the park late at night or pushing his heart to the limit with beer, cigarettes and junk food. When it comes to fighting for his country, he doesn't turn and run; instead, he grits his teeth and marches straight into the hail of fire. In *Terminator 2*, you don't see Arnold Schwarzenegger shaking in his boots when the 'baddy' comes after him. Of course, that's probably because he's an android, but when it comes to fear, it sometimes seems as if all men are supposed to behave more like machines than human beings.

And, finally, the real man is always on top when it comes to sex. He's a *great lover*. That's why Richard Gere is envied by so many other men. There's no doubting his great sexual power over women: not only has he been seen giving women shuddering orgasms in almost all his films, he's also considered desirable by millions of women across the world and ended up marrying one of the most beautiful (even if it didn't work out). It seems anyone aspiring to be a real man must have women falling at his feet. A gigantic penis, never-ending orgasms and a thrust rate that would put a pneumatic drill to shame also help.

But – and this is a very big 'but' – sleeping around only earns you points as a real man if the people you're having sex with are women. If you're gay, you can expect to be refused membership of the real-men's club, no matter what your other talents. Real men wouldn't dream of spending a night with another man or even touching him, unless it was to deliver a fatal karate chop to his neck. It's certainly hard to imagine a James Bond film ending with him snuggling beneath the duvet with weapons' boffin 'Q' rather than Pussy Galore, Honey Ryder or any of the other 'Bond girls'.

## the inner arnie

No matter how caring, sharing and sandal-wearing we might be, it's more than probable that each of us has a little real man inside our head – an internal Arnold Schwarzenegger perhaps – reminding us how a man should be. The size and nature of this 'inner Arnie' might vary from man to man – reflecting differences in personal history, ethnicity or social class – but if we listen closely enough, we're almost certain to hear that Austrian mumble, urging us to be strong, powerful and always in control. And if another character should dare to enter our mind – perhaps with a softer, gentler voice – then it's likely to be a case of (in those immortal words of the Terminator) 'Fuck you, arsehole.'

The key question is where did this inner Arnie come from? Were we born with him already hard-wired or did he take up residence later? In other words, is it 'nature' or 'nurture' that's responsible for the real-man syndrome? Over the last hundred years or so, the cases for both nature and nurture have been strongly argued. The more traditional view is that the inner Arnie forms an innate part of men's biological make-up. According to this 'biological determinist' perspective, the traits of the real man are rooted in the evolutionary process – those 11 males who were more dominant, aggressive and sexually promiscuous were more likely to mate and hence pass down their genetic material (containing their real-man characteristics) to subsequent generations. Men who were sensitive, emotional and passive tended to lose out in the struggle for the survival of the fittest. Being less likely to attract a female partner, let alone impregnate her with their substandard and 'unmanly' genes, their characteristics would have slowly died out.

The behaviour of other animals is often used to support this argument. Male rhesus monkeys (one of our closest animal relatives), for instance, are instinctively aggressive, fight for dominance and threaten each other within a few months of their birth. It's also been widely suggested there's a close link between aggressive behaviour and the male sex hormone, testosterone. Female rhesus monkeys injected with testosterone exhibit more domineering and aggressive behaviour and human females exposed to testosterone before birth become more energetic, athletic, 'tomboyish' and careerminded than other girls. Men who have committed violent crime have been found to have higher levels of testosterone surging through their veins. Brain differences between men and women – females are thought to have a larger connecting structure between the two hemispheres and to use more of their brain to carry out certain mental tasks – have also been ascribed to the influence of sex hormones.

The biological perspective has been severely criticized, however. There are clear limits as to how far human and animal behaviour can be compared, not least because animal studies point in many different directions. In some bird species, for example, the males take the major responsibility for incubating eggs; among marmosets, the fathers carry the young more often than the mother. There may be a tendency, too, for the biological determinists to confuse correlation with causation – while high testosterone levels may make men behave more aggressively, it's also been established that aggressive behaviour increases testosterone levels. Brain differences, if they actually exist (and not all neuroscientists are sure), may reflect differences in learning and experience. It's known that rats, for instance, raised in a stimulating environment – a large cage with many other rats and toys rather than a small isolated cage – end up with a thicker and more complex cerebral cortex.

The biological perspective also fails to explain why male behaviour and ideals can vary so much. If the process of evolution had, over countless millennia, taken its inevitable course and weeded out all the wimps, by now virtually all men would be like Bruce Willis and 90 per cent of America reduced to rubble. This clearly hasn't happened, at least not yet. Even within our own culture of modern Western society, there are clearly many different types of man, from the highly aggressive to the very gentle. The differences between cultures can be even greater. In the Tchambuli tribe of New Guinea, for instance, women control the households, make all major decisions and do the work, while men spend their time painting, dancing, carving and gossiping. Some anthropologists **13** have argued that, thousands of years ago, many more cultures were matriarchies (societies dominated by women rather than men). All this suggests that the inner Arnie can't be a purely natural or innate phenomenon, but must be closely linked to cultural and historical factors.

The theories of the biological determinists are opposed by those who believe the characteristics of the real man to be a direct product of social forces. These 'social determinists' argue that young boys are brought up or 'conditioned' to behave in typically masculine ways. If they cry or play with dolls, they are told off or punished, while fighting or domineering behaviour is rewarded by parental and peer approval. Boys therefore grow up trying to emulate the real man in the hope of earning love, admiration and rewards from others. They avoid unmanly behaviour, even though it's an integral part of their humanity, because they've learnt that this can lead to humiliation or even pain.

It's also argued that boys learn to be real men by observing and attempting to copy the behaviour of adult males. A young boy, for instance, sees his father acting unemotionally, aggressively and competitively, and thinks (perhaps unawarely), 'That's how I should be.' And, of course, it's not just parents who act as models for young males. When a child sees the phaser-wielding James T. Kirk boldly battling with Klingons and Romulans – and getting laid for his troubles – it's not difficult to see how he can come to believe that if a Starship captain can be loved for being powerful and strong, then so can he.

There's now a great deal of research demonstrating the different ways in which boys and girls are treated at an early age. For example, when psychologists dressed a baby in blue (to give the impression it was a boy), they found it was bounced around and stimulated more by adults than the same baby wrapped in pink (to give the impression it was a girl). It's well-established that boys are given toy animals or vehicles, and later guns, to play with while girls are given dolls and fabric (even though 12-month-old boys are actually more likely to play with dolls than girls of a similar age). Similarly, in allocating household chores, boys are often given tasks that take them out of the house – such as work in the garden or taking out the rubbish – while girls are given domestic tasks like baby-sitting, cooking or washing up.

However, the social determinists still need to explain how and why the characteristics of the real man emerged in the first place. If they're not innate, where did they come from? One suggestion is that they're rooted in prehistoric human behaviour. Imagine the scene: the tribe is sitting round the cave and, as usual, they're starving. The berries they've been scavenging lack protein; and while the mice, lizards and termites caught near home might be tastier, they still constitute little more than a Neanderthal vol-au-vent. It's definitely time to hunt some sabre-toothed tiger burgers, but who's going to do it? Because the women might well be breast-feeding or burdened by pregnancy, it wouldn't make much sense for them to spend days away from the cave chasing animals. So the men got the job, and because a hunter needed to be strong, aggressive, **15** unemotional and courageous, these characteristics came to be admired in men. A Neanderthal Woody Allen might have made people laugh around the cave fire, but a Palaeolithic Jean-Claude Van Damme who came home with a brontosaurus under each arm would have been seen as a lot more valuable. Men who could adapt their hunting skills to defending the tribe against marauders would also have made an enormous contribution to the community's welfare. So men learnt that if they wanted to be loved, respected and desired, they needed to be fearless, strong and protective – and these are the values that came to be passed down from generation to generation.

There are some problems, however, with the argument that it's all down to nurture. First, the social determinists present a rather passive model of psychological development, suggesting that young boys are like Plasticine figures that get shaped and moulded by society without any will of their own. Secondly, their theory's hard-pressed to explain away all of the biological evidence. It's undeniably true that, in most animal species, the male is more aggressive than the female. The fact that men across the overwhelming majority of cultures tend to share similar characteristics is also difficult to explain by social factors alone. What's more, many parents who have tried to bring up their sons in non-traditional ways have been shocked to discover that, as soon as they go to school, they quickly start behaving like all the other young males, trading their vegan rice cakes for Power Ranger stickers.

Both the biological and social explanations for the origins of masculinity can become rigid and even politically motivated. Indeed, the origins of gender roles is an incredibly heated area of academic debate and there's always the danger that genuine discussion and exploration can become obscured by the desire of researchers to prove that what they want to believe is true. For instance, it tends to be right-wing researchers who incline towards the biological determinist perspective, while socialist and feminist writers generally prefer social explanations. That's why many sociologists and psychologists are now rejecting a clear-cut explanation for gender roles. Instead, they've come to the conclusion that the real man is neither a product of exclusively biological or exclusively social forces. Rather, he comes from a complicated interaction of both innate and learned factors.

It may be, for example, that men's generally greater physical strength – a biological result of testosterone, the hormone that stimulates muscle development – became encouraged by social factors. Because women's childcare responsibilities meant that they couldn't so readily hunt or fight, men's strength became seen as increasingly important. And because men were expected to be strong, they were taught to behave in ways that increased their testosterone levels and their muscle growth. It is difficult to say precisely how much of this complex process is due to nature and how much to nurture, but most psychologists now believe social factors account for the greater part of how men are. So while the inner Arnie might partly be rooted in our biological heritage, his **17** psychological dominance is undoubtedly due to environmental circumstances – which allows us immense potential for change.

## men for change

It's understandable that men in prehistoric societies needed to be aggressive, self-sufficient and unemotional. That seemed the best way of guaranteeing the tribe's survival. But in the modern world, where hard disks have replaced hunting and where women can be back to work within a few weeks of giving birth, we no longer need men who can emulate Arnie. Men who can chase after and slaughter gazelles are now less useful than men who care about the world and those who live in it, including themselves. The real man ideal is now redundant and out-of-date. Our inner Arnie has done so many leg-curls, triceps dips and bench presses, that it's time he took a break – preferably a long one. In fact, it seems even Arnie himself no longer wants to listen to his inner Arnie. Present at the birth of his daughter, Conan the Babysitter even cut the umbilical cord himself and later claimed to enjoy changing nappies and getting up in the night to rock her to sleep. And Mr Schwarzenegger's not alone. That other modern male icon, Clint Eastwood, has also decided it's time for a change, as anyone who saw his eyes water in *In The Line Of Fire* will know.

In the last 25 years, in fact, at the same time as women have begun to shake off the restrictions of traditional femininity, many men have felt it's OK to ease up on trying to be 'manly'.

Active fathering, talking about feelings – even crying – all now seem to be more acceptable than ever before. The last five years in particular have seen a real upsurge in discussions of men and masculinity – in magazines, newspapers and books, on television and radio, even in universities – and it seems likely that this awareness of men's issues will continue to flourish and alternatives to traditional masculinity will be put forward.

The modern man, then, has a unique opportunity to take off the real-man mask and explore different – and potentially more enjoyable – ways of being male. This doesn't mean that we can't be strong, independent and even aggressive any more; it's just that we don't have to be like that all the time. We can still be fiery on the football pitch and protective of our family, but also intimate with our partners and vulnerable with our friends. We can begin to respond with flexibility and freshness to every situation and, instead of being stuck behind one rigid mask, we can start to explore and express the full complexity of our being.

But how can we kick off the process of change? Most importantly, we first need to uncover and understand our inner Arnie. And that's not necessarily easy. The effects of our male upbringing started early and run deep. Much of the time we're not even aware of when the inner Arnie is operating or what he's telling us – it just seems natural for us to stop ourselves crying or to react to a provocation by trying to look 'hard'. We're a bit like actors who've played the same stage role for so long that we've incorporated it into our daily lives. Much of 19 this book, therefore, is about the kinds of things that the inner real man might be telling us. The more we can recognize when he's talking and what he's saying, the more opportunity we'll have to stand back from him and decide whether or not to obey his commands. By coming to know our inner Arnie better, we can begin to control him, rather than allowing him to control us.

But it's not always easy to go against the inner Arnie – it's not like trying to re-format a computer hard disk at the touch of a button. He's powerful, not only because he symbolizes centuries of male identity, but also because he's helped us to function, survive and succeed in a 'man's world'. So if we decide we want to share our fears and vulnerabilities with our mates, it'll be no surprise if the inner Arnie responds by flexing his pecs and telling us, 'I'll be back.' Letting go of long-established attitudes and behaviours can be a frightening step into the unknown. But the more we take risks, the more we can discover the benefits of change. Ironically enough, the process of taking off the real-man mask often requires the kind of courage and mettle the real man most stands for.

Of course, our friends might think we're a 'woosie' if we try to change. They may well believe that men should be manly too, and any wimpy behaviour risks severe condemnation. That's why it can be important to try to make contact with other men who are also trying to change; their support and encouragement can be invaluable in helping us to 'unmask'. If we know we won't be put down for experimenting with our masculinity, and if we know other men are doing it as well, the whole process can seem a lot less daunting.

Ultimately, however, there's only one sure way to change – to actually give it a go. If we want to start ordering non-alcoholic beer, then we have to take the risk. If we want to relax when we're making love, we have to put the mental calculations to one side. If we want to stop beating up our partner, we have to let go of our need for dominance. Of course, when we give up our pursuit of the real-man ideal, we may well feel swamped by all the fears that have been holding us back for years. But, as the saying goes, we can 'Feel the fear and do it anyway.' Or, in hard-core bodybuilder language, 'No pain, no gain.'

Yet we're under no compulsion to make these initial break-throughs as traumatic as possible. We don't need to burst into tears in the middle of a supermarket to work through our emotional blockages, or start changing nappies on the back seat of a bus to prove we're an involved dad. There are easier ways of changing our behaviour and this book includes many tried and tested techniques men have followed – and lived to tell the tale. Some of the suggestions you may find valuable; others you may think are just plain daft. Don't feel compelled to try anything that doesn't feel right for you but, at the same time, don't be afraid to experiment. Perhaps what's most encouraging is the fact that more and more men are beginning to change. These are not men who are substituting an 'inner wimp' for an inner Arnie, but men who are beginning to realize that they can be strong *and* tender, emotional *and* brave, loving *and* independent, intimate *and* forceful. The road to a more 'rounded', complete masculinity is certainly not without its hazards, but many men are now beginning to recognize how fulfilling the journey can be.

# emotions:
# the feeling man

## the spock syndrome

What's the worst thing about being male? Not being able to urinate when you've got an erection? Losing your hair just when you really start to believe you're attractive? Disposable razors that cut your face to pieces? Perhaps, but for many men, the worst thing about being male is an inability to get in touch with our emotions. Sometimes, it can feel as if we're covered from head to foot with bubble wrap. We don't feel sadness when a loved one dies; we feel numb. We don't feel happiness when we become a father; we feel numb. We don't act excited when we get the job we've longed for; we just feel numb, numb, numb. And men aren't the only ones who yearn for greater male emotionality. Many women, too, complain that their partners are about as emotional as Mr Spock – they never, ever say how they're feeling. What's worse, we can't kill people with the Vulcan death-grip either!

Our problem is that while part of us may want to be more emotional, the inner Arnie isn't so keen. When we're emotional, we're not in complete control of our behaviour –   23 and that contravenes the real man's first commandment. Fear can stop us walking down a dark alley at night, grief can make us bawl uncontrollably, joy can make us helplessly jump up and down. So the real man, the man who's in complete control of his behaviour, can't afford to 'let go' and display any feelings. Like Roger Moore's James Bond, the ultimate symbol of male emotional sterility, there's no room for fear, love or rage. Whether he's being chased after, thanked by the Queen or made love to, the only display Moore allows himself is an arched eyebrow. It's a face that says, 'Nothing can affect me. I'm in charge here. I'm a real man.' (It also says, of course, quite a lot about his acting ability.)

Psychologists have demonstrated the extent of men's emotional repression. While seven- and eight-year-old boys and girls don't seem to differ much when it comes to express- ing their feelings, a huge gulf has opened up by mid- adolescence. Indeed, teenage boys are much more likely than girls to deny ever having any emotional experiences. In a review of many investigations of gender differences, one researcher failed to find a single study which showed males disclosed more personal or intimate information than females. Men seem to prefer to rely on their intellect, logic and rational- ity as a guide to life, contrasting themselves with women who are just 'too sensitive' or 'over emotional'.

There are several techniques most of us use to repress our emotions. Let's look at an example. Suppose we've just split up with our partner. At first, the chances are we'll feel pretty bad about it, but if we feel the emotions are threatening our sense of masculine control, then we might deal with them in one of the following ways:

- **Intellectualization:** *keeping everything on the rational plane and trying to deal with feelings by thinking or talking about them in an abstract way. So we might say to ourselves, 'Relationships aren't really that important,' or 'There's plenty more fish in the sea.'*
- **Avoidance:** *switching our attention onto something else every time we think about our partner, or keeping ourselves busy with work and sport.*
- **Denial:** *pretending we're not feeling anything, telling ourselves and others that everything's OK.*
- **Demonizing:** *exaggerating our partner's faults to help us feel better. We might even end up totally blaming her for the separation even though we were both responsible.*
- **Drugs:** *using substances to numb our feelings, like going out and getting drunk or stoned.*

Often we use a mixture of these techniques (and others) to deal with a wide range of uncomfortable emotional experiences. Over time, we can reach a point where we lose touch with what our emotions actually are. We find it hard to know whether we're feeling happy, sad, angry or ashamed. We no longer have a language with which to recognize or talk about our emotions. We become, as some psychologists put it, 'emotionally illiterate'. Moreover, the longer we repress our feelings, the more they become a terrifying unknown 25 and the more inclined we are to try to keep them out of our mind.

Repressing our emotions might satisfy the inner Arnie, but there are a number of reasons why this kind of behaviour probably isn't such a good idea. For a start, emotions represent a physiological response that has evolved over millions of years as a means of helping us to function effectively. When we feel fear, for instance, it's because our body is telling us something dangerous is about to happen; when we feel joy, it's our body telling us we're doing something it likes. Emotions are like a radar that gives us information about the state of the world outside. If we don't listen to our feelings, we're like a plane without any detection equipment, and sooner or later we're likely to crash into a lot of hazards. We repress our fear of dying, so we carry on smoking and drinking; we repress our rage, so we carry on letting people walk all over us; we repress a sense of guilt from humiliating a colleague, so we end up hurting him again and again. Once we start listening to our feelings, we can begin to go round the hazards instead of into them.

What's more, if we repress our emotions, they don't just disappear. Rather, they can continue to affect us in ways we're not aware of. So we might deny or avoid any feelings of grief after finishing a relationship, but that hurt can still bubble away inside of us – perhaps pushing us too soon into a new relationship as a way of neutralizing the pain, or making us avoid another relationship to ensure that we don't get hurt again. And, if we've been stifling our emotions from our early years, a mass of repressed feelings from boyhood are likely to be having a substantial impact on our lives. In other words, denying our emotions is like refusing to open our bank statements because we know we have an overdraft – it doesn't go away, it just accumulates interest.

Furthermore, although our emotions are a useful guide to action, we won't always want to follow them. The more we repress our feelings, however, the less choice we actually have. For example, our fear might stop us being assertive with our boss, even though we know it's not in our interests to avoid confronting him. But if we refuse to admit to ourselves how frightened we are, we'll find ways of avoiding what scares us: perhaps persuading ourselves that we're making a fuss about nothing or never quite finding the right time to do it. If we can acknowledge our fear, however, we can stop making excuses and start tackling the real issue. We can make a conscious choice to talk to our boss even though we know we're scared. While we can't control what we don't acknowledge, what we don't acknowledge can still control us.

Not dealing with grief and other emotions can also lead to health problems. When we keep emotions repressed, they eat away at our insides – almost literally – contributing to stress-related illnesses such as ulcers, heart disease and cancer. According to One plus One, the marriage and partnership research organization, divorced and separated men are more likely than women to die early or to suffer illnesses, and this may be because men tend to be worse than women at dealing with loss. The Samaritans have also attributed the recent increase in the suicide rate of young males to men's difficulties with expressing emotions.

Finally, denying our emotions can also have a detrimental impact on our relationships with others. If a man's feeling angry with his partner for not sharing the washing-up, for instance, but refuses to tell her why he's angry (because he can't admit his anger to himself), the chances are he'll find other ways of expressing it. So he punishes her by 'the silent treatment', or by going down the pub with his mates or by not doing the washing-up himself. And if she doesn't know why he's angry, she's either going to be frantically guessing at the cause or feeling unjustifiably criticized. So she might start doing things to punish him, initiating a vicious circle that could well end in arguments, fighting or worse. On the other hand, if he could simply say to her, 'I feel angry with you because you don't do the washing-up', then she at least would know what was going on. If his anger is justified, she might change her behaviour or, if she feels his anger is unfair, they can then talk adult-to-adult about who does how much washing-up and find a mutually agreeable solution. Either way, it's only when the underlying feelings are expressed that effective choices can be made.

# the world of emotions

## fear

Up in the Scottish highlands on a freezing spring morning, John, a 25-year-old student, decided with a few friends to go on a hike:

> However, when we got to the mountain we intended to walk around, we realized the path was covered in snow. Denise, the only woman in our party, decided to turn around and go back. I was pretty scared but I thought to myself, 'What the hell, the other guys are going. I may as well too.' I guess at the time I thought it was a bit of fun, but I also didn't want to seem like a wimp by turning round and going home.

John's only problem was that he was totally ill-equipped. He didn't have proper waterproof clothing or the right footwear, and within a few hours he was freezing cold:

> My ankle-high monkey boots had filled up with snow and I could barely feel my feet. With every step, I plunged waist-deep into the snow. It was horrible, and I had no idea how much further we had to go. About four hours later, when it began to get dark, we looked at the map and realized with absolute horror that we were only halfway round. It meant we'd be walking through the snow in

29

the dark. I was terrified. I was convinced I'd never make it.

Fortunately their map-reading skills were as inadequate as their clothing. A few minutes later they saw a road – a safe route back to their hostel. 'It was such a relief and I was dying to tell Denise about our adventure,' says John. 'But it was a pretty stupid thing to do.'

Fear is probably the emotion most feared by men – and the most repressed. As John knows only too well, the risk of appearing a sissy, a coward or 'yellow' is enough to spur even the most gentle of men to stand up for himself, let alone the cowboy swigging whisky from his hip flask. For hundreds of years, a man challenged to a duel had no alternative but to protect his honour and risk his life. To express fear or uncertainty would have marked out him and his family for ridicule and humiliation. During the First World War, many men who didn't volunteer to fight were sent white feathers to signify their cowardice.

Fearlessness seems to be a universally glorified male trait. Japanese Kamikaze pilots hurtled to their death for honour and Emperor regardless of their own terror. In Africa, each adolescent boy of the Northern Kenyan Samburu tribe is placed before his male relatives and prospective in-laws and has his foreskin severed during an initiation ritual. As the piece of skin is cut off, an operation that may take as long as four minutes, the boy must show absolutely no sign of fear or pain. If he makes the slightest twitch he will be excluded from his peers and bear a scar of inferiority for the rest of his life. Not only that, his whole family and lineage will be shamed forever.

## sadness

'Big boys don't cry' – and that's a fact. Research shows that the average woman cries far more than the average man. One study of 600 students at a California university found that 89 per cent of the women said they cried either occasionally, frequently or very frequently, compared with just 29 per cent of the men. Another study of 680 American couples aged 18–65 found that 19 per cent of the women said they had cried in the last week, while just 3 per cent of the men had done so.

'Stop sniffling,' we were probably told as kids, 'crying won't get you anywhere.' Well, it probably did – put down or beaten up. As young boys, crying was one of the most taboo things we could do. Most of us learnt very quickly to swallow our tears and put on a brave face. Consequently, many of us find it hard to remember the last time we had a good cry. We may have the odd snuffle here and there but a deep, gut-wrenching barrage of sobs is way beyond our repertoire.

So many of us men avoid feeling the full extent of our sadness. We're afraid of expressing our grief and when painful feelings come up, we try to keep them down rather than letting them out. Grieving is a natural response to loss, however, and unless we accept and experience the pain, we'll find it difficult to move on. Beginning a new relationship **31** before we've come to terms with ending the previous one is like starting a new Agatha Christie novel when we still haven't found out who the murderer was in the book before. So we get confused. Perhaps we expect our new lover to behave in the same ways as our old one, or we might start getting angry and irritated with our new lover for doing or not doing the same things as our previous partner. And if we don't properly grieve the new relationship when that finishes, we can end up dumping all the accumulated problems onto yet another person.

Because grief can be carried from one relationship to the next, it's vital that we work through any sadness lingering from the beginning of the chain – our relationship with our parents. Those of us with loving, caring parents, may have never fully mourned the warmth and security that we lost when we grew to adult independence. And those of us with abusive, uncaring parents may have never mourned the love we never had. Because of this, many of us grow up carrying a burden of grief and still expect to be parented and nurtured in new relation-ships. By talking about our sadness, exploring it and letting it out, we can enter new relationships afresh and clear away the unhappiness that's been clogging up our brains.

If sadness or grief isn't dealt with, there's always the danger that it can end up sliding into depression. This is more than feeling down for a day or two. Depression is, well, depressing: it drags on, you feel you can't cope, it sometimes makes life feel barely worth living. Common symptoms include sleepless-ness, feelings of inadequacy or even thoughts of suicide. Over one fifth of people say they've experienced depression and, although some people benefit from taking antidepressant drugs, most psychiatrists agree that talking about your worries, reliving painful experiences and having a good cry are part of the body's natural healing mechanism.

## joy

Because being happy means relinquishing control, it can sometimes be as tough as grieving. When someone goes down on us, for instance, we need to relax, allowing the other person to take charge. The same fear of letting go can inhibit us from expressing our happiness. If we started leaping up and down in our seats when we watched *True Lies,* or screaming with delight when a partner first says she loves us, we'd probably be terrified other people would think we're a pillock. Not surprisingly then, one of the few times many of us do show joy is when we're drunk – then, and almost only then, can we put our arms around each other and dance at the bar. It takes a lot of booze before many of us can finally let go and admit we're happy.

## shame

Shame can be a useful indicator of when we've transgressed our moral codes, but it's also the prison warder who keeps men locked in the cell of masculinity. With so much pressure to live up to a manly ideal, many of us experience profound feelings of humiliation, embarrassment and disgrace. If we aren't muscular enough, we feel ashamed of being a wimp; if we don't have a girlfriend, we're ashamed of being a nerd; if we don't have a decent job, we're ashamed of being a 'loser'. However arrogant or certain we may seem to others, shame is often written large at the back of our minds. It can also keep us timid and passive, too frightened to do anything that might draw attention to what we perceive as our 'inadequacies'. And because the inner Arnie is so often concerned with doing things for others – protecting, defending, providing for – we might often experience profound feelings of guilt. We feel guilty for not providing our family with a decent standard of living; we feel guilty for not standing up for our girlfriend when she gets insulted in a pub; we feel guilty for not being a perfect gentleman and ringing a woman back after a one-night stand.

## jealousy

How does it feel if your boss at work is ten years younger than you? Or if your partner runs off with a man who's suaver, richer and more handsome than you could ever be? There will always be some men who are doing a lot better than us in the real-man sweepstakes – with bigger houses, bigger cars, bigger salaries and, no doubt, bigger penises. Seeing these men can bring up deep feelings of jealousy, reminding us of our own sense of failure as a man.

We can also be jealous of women, of course. Sometimes this

can be because they seem better at being a man than us – they might have a better job or even bigger biceps. But sometimes we can also be jealous of their femininity – that they are allowed to show their emotions more easily, that they seem to feel things more powerfully, that they can experience great intimacy with their friends and certainly with their children. We may even envy their sexuality – that they're much more able to display their bodies and to be openly desired and pursued.

## anger

At first sight, anger may seem like one emotion men are pretty good at and, compared with other emotions, that's probably true. When we're angry we might momentarily lose control, but anger is one of the few emotions that can actually increase our power in the long run. After all, flying off into fits of rage is an effective way of frightening people into doing what we want. For many of Hollywood's male icons, the only emotion they ever seem to express is anger – and it never seems to lose them any friends. When Mel Gibson in *Braveheart*, the film epic about Scottish independence, realizes that his wife has been murdered, he doesn't waste valuable celluloid grieving. Instead, his rage transforms him from peace-loving farmer into a warrior who inspires his nation and terrifies the English oppressors.

Because anger is so notoriously associated with masculinity, some new men have gone to the opposite extreme and attempted to repress their rage completely. On the emotional compass, however, anger points to a feeling that we're not getting what we want – perhaps even that we're being mistreated. So trying to pretend we never get angry is like pretending we never get hurt. Being angry doesn't mean we have to be violent. Rather, finding ways of expressing our anger honestly and non-aggressively can be much more useful.

## there's an emotion in there somewhere

Fortunately, it's becoming increasingly acceptable for men to express their feelings. Just think about how unremarkable it seemed when Andre Agassi wept after he'd won the Wimbledon tennis championship in 1992. Being more honest with ourselves is a crucial first step in this process and there are several specific techniques we can use to gain a deeper insight into our emotions.

- **Keep a diary:** *write down what happens to you and how you're feeling from day-to-day. Try to explore what prompts particular feelings.*
- **Change the way you talk:** *encourage yourself to be more emotionally open with friends and lovers. Use the word 'feel' rather than 'think' when you're talking. Also try to talk in the first person ('I') rather than the more abstract 'we', 'one' or 'you'.*
- **Reflect on your feelings regularly:** *stop yourself in the middle of the day and ask yourself, 'How am I feeling right now?' The answer may be 'bored', 'OK', or 'not*

much', but practise being as honest as you can. Be aware
of any 'shoulds', 'oughts' or 'musts' in your head that are
luring you into misreporting your feelings.

- **Spend time with people who accept your emotions:** we
often hide our feelings because we believe, sometimes
quite accurately, that the people we're with will tease
and humiliate us if we show fear, sadness or joy.

- **Write an 'open' letter:** be totally honest about your
feelings to a friend, partner or even to yourself. Get it
all out – at the end of the day, there's no obligation to
send it off.

- **Try to let go:** go with your emotions the next time you
feel them welling up, rather than trying to hold them
back. It may even mean bursting into tears when you're
watching Oprah. Little by little, see how emotionally
expressive you can allow yourself to be. Perhaps start on
your own – it'll then be easier when you're with a
partner or a close friend.

## seeing a shrink

Many people dismiss therapy or counselling as something they
would never, ever do. They imagine it's only for lunatics or
New Yorkers and believe that men should somehow be able to
sort themselves out without outside help. Nevertheless, a
huge range of people are now using therapy and counselling
(terms which tend to be used interchangeably). These are
often individuals who have no specific problem but just want **37**

to find out more about themselves and take greater control of their lives. It can be an excellent way of helping us get more in touch with our feelings, but it can be particularly helpful for those who've just been through a major emotional upset, such as the end of a relationship or a bereavement.

The basic premise of therapy is that each of us has parts of ourselves that we're not aware of and, for as long as they remain unacknowledged, they will affect us in ways over which we have no control. It's only by bringing those parts into conscious awareness that we can develop a greater sense of self-understanding, power and determination over our lives. This process is also what can make therapy such a frightening prospect. It can require the courage to look at our life and our past, including the painful bits most of us would rather forget or pretend never happened. We may end up remembering things that, for a time, could be worrying or upsetting. However these memories have probably always been there affecting our lives and it may only be by exploring them that a process of change can take place.

The role of the therapist is to help us in this process of understanding and change, either by encouraging us to talk, pointing us in the right direction, teaching us models and techniques we could find useful or just listening. Contrary to the popular image of therapy, there are very few therapists who require the client to lie on a couch while they analyse away before providing some magic solution. The role of the therapist is much more facilitator than guru.

There are many different kinds of therapy, each with

different models of how the mind works, how it's disturbed, and how it can be 'put back in place'. Sigmund Freud's original model, *psychoanalysis*, is still practised today, although there are now several different schools of Freudian analysis. Freud's basic idea was that the selfish, childish parts of our mind (the *id*) need to be repressed by a more parental part (the *super-ego*) in order that we can function in society. The conflicts between these two factions are mediated by the *ego* – the decision-making part of the mind. Freudian therapy uses techniques such as dream-analysis and word-association to bring to consciousness the hidden, unconscious parts of the mind, so that they no longer effect us in ways about which we are unaware. *Psychoanalytic psychotherapy* has become the most commonly practised version of psychoanalysis. It involves seeing a therapist once, sometimes twice, a week probably for at least six months. In fact, many people remain in therapy for several years. While it can be effective, it's also expensive as well as time-consuming.

In his early work, Freud believed that traumas in the first few years of life can affect us later on, and that we need to 'relive' those experiences so that we can exorcize ourselves of the pain associated with them. This is still the basic philosophy behind a number of different schools of therapy today, particularly *re-evaluation co-counselling*. Co-counselling encourages clients to 'discharge' their 'early hurts' in order to help them live more 'rationally'. It's unique among therapies in that clients counsel each other rather than having a professional therapist doing all the work. This has the obvious advantage of being cheap, but it also has the disadvantage that the counsellor might not always be able to deal with what the client is going through – which has the potential to be quite risky. Co-counselling pays a lot of attention to the social and economic influences on people's personal lives, and to the fact that certain groups have been oppressed by society, factors often neglected in other types of therapy. Co-counselling runs men's support groups and workshops where men explore the ways that they as men have been affected by social conditioning. Co-counselling can be particularly useful for men because of its emphasis on getting in touch with feelings.

*Non-directive* or *client-centred counselling* was developed by Carl Rogers in the 1950s and is now one of the most widespread forms of therapy. As the name suggests, the client is pretty much in charge of how the session goes and the counsellor spends most of their time listening appreciatively and reflecting back the client's comments in a way that helps them to be better explored and understood. The basic premise is that if the counsellor can be empathetic, honest and express 'unconditional positive regard', the client will begin to let down the 'false self' mask and to be who they 'really' are. Non-directive counselling can be very valuable and supportive, although it can also be frustrating for those expecting direct feedback.

Another useful form of therapy is called *gestalt therapy*. This focuses on the here-and-now emotions and feelings of the person rather than looking at their past. It uses a number of different techniques, such as talking to chairs or different parts of the body, to help a person become more aware of their conscious existence. This may sound ridiculous, but many of those who have done it vouch for its effectiveness. Gestalt therapy is particularly useful for men since it helps us to focus on exactly what is going on in the moment, teaching us to become more aware of our emotional feelings and bodily sensations as they are happening.

*Existential-phenomenological psychotherapies* are also focused on the here-and-now, but unlike gestalt therapy, have no model of how individuals should be. Clients are not encouraged to 'realize their true potential' but to clarify and understand their experience of 'being in the world' – whether it's happy, miserable, anxious or schizophrenic – and to make choices about how they want to be. These therapies reject the use of specific 'techniques'. Instead, the therapist attempts to enter into a person-to-person dialogue with the client, listening, clarifying, highlighting paradoxes and 'patterns' and helping the client to explore their choices. Existential-phenomenological therapies are unique in that they do not try to push men into one particular way of being, although they can be disappointing for those who like more cathartic and energetic approaches.

*Transactional analysis* (TA) is a form of therapy that divides the person up into 'parent' (moralizing), 'adult' (rational) and 'child' ('I want'), and looks at their life in terms of the interaction between these three different parts of the personality. TA also looks at the way we interact with other people's parent–adult–child and the games that we play with them. TA is a very useful model and offers some particularly refreshing insights, although at times the therapy can be a bit too analytical and not be a good idea for men who find it easy to talk about themselves but much harder to get deeply into their feelings.

There are also a number of more modern creative-based therapies including *art therapy*, *drama therapy*, *dance therapy* and *music therapy*. These can be very effective – sometimes a red splodge on a piece of paper can reveal far more than words ever can. The therapist may help you to examine and analyse a piece of art or music you've created, but often it's the act of being creative itself that's seen as most therapeutic. Creative-based therapies frequently take place in groups and are sometimes incorporated into other types of one-to-one therapy. They can be good for men because they stop us over-intellectualizing and help us to be more spontaneous, something we often find very hard.

It's important to note that while some therapists stick rigidly to a specific therapeutic model, many practitioners are now eclectic about their choice of techniques, picking and choosing from a whole array of approaches. However often what's just as important as choosing the right approach is choosing the right therapist. That's why it's important for us not to choose the first person we find out about but to shop around. After all, we almost certainly wouldn't buy the first pair of football boots we tried on and a therapist will cost us a lot more – and may well become a much more significant part of our life.

If you're interested in therapy, think about what kind of

therapist you want. Would you prefer a man or a woman? Someone older than you or about the same age? What sort of therapeutic technique appeals most? It's sometimes possible to go on short therapy workshops which can give you an idea of the different approaches. Unless it's co-counselling you're after, your best bet is to contact one of the professional therapy agencies and get their list of members. At present, anyone can call themselves a 'therapist', so it's advisable to make sure that the person you see is professionally qualified. Arrange an initial meeting (which you'll usually be charged for) to see how you get on and be straight about what you want. Talk about any doubts you may have. Be clear about how much you can afford to pay and, if you're low-waged, find out whether they offer a sliding scale of fees. If you don't think a therapist is right for you, you needn't feel under any obligation to see them again.

Many therapies can also take place in a group setting. This has the basic advantage of being cheaper and of helping you to learn about how you behave with other people, which often provides insights into how we experienced our families when we were children. However, a group obviously cannot provide the level of individual attention you'd receive in a one-to-one relationship with a therapist.

## away the lads

Another way of exploring your emotional life – and, indeed, every aspect of what it means to be a man – is through a    43 men's group. Although men often spend a lot of time together – at work, in the pub, playing sport – we often find it hard to talk honestly to each other about our thoughts and feelings. If we can put to one side the feeling that it's weird, naff or wimpy to be in a men's group, then it can be a good place to take real steps to break out of the masculine straitjacket.

Although there are different types of groups, the most common focus on 'personal growth'. The basic aim is to improve the quality of men's lives through basic counselling and therapeutic techniques – sharing feelings, looking at group dynamics, talking about childhood experiences. Typical issues explored might include relationships with parents, sexuality, competition with other men, violence, work or health. Personal growth groups can be very good for helping us to get in touch with our feelings and to get closer to other men. However, some men have found these groups too 'soft' or self-indulgent and prefer men's groups that look at the positive, as well as the negative, aspects of being a man.

More recently, the 'mythopoetic' men's group has become popular. These are based mainly on the work of Robert Bly, author of the best-selling book *Iron John: A Book About Men*. Mythopoetic groups use traditional initiation rites, ancient legends and contact with nature to try to put men in touch with a more 'authentic' kind of masculinity. Such groups have also been much, and unfairly, mocked in the media, with suggestions that all men do is roll around in mud, hug trees and sniff each other's bottoms. Many men who've been to mythopoetic groups have, in fact, found them very powerful – particularly in the ways they have explored men's relationships with their fathers – although such groups have also been criticized for reinforcing many traditional masculine characteristics.

Joining a men's group of any sort, however, is not necessarily straightforward. While many major cities now have at least one group, it's likely to be small, have a closed membership and not to advertise for new members. Perhaps the best way of finding out about existing groups – or to meet other men who might be interested in starting a new group with you – is to attend a men's workshop, therapy group, conference or evening class. Details are often available from magazines which cover men's or personal growth issues. Most groups meet for two or three hours, once or twice a month. Some meet over a fixed period – perhaps six months – while others meet over several years or even indefinitely.

Another alternative is to set up your own group. A useful first step is to think about what you want to get out of a group. Then you'll need to recruit around four to ten men who share your aims. These could be friends and colleagues, or you could try contacting other men through 'alternative' men's magazines and workshops. Once you've got a group together, you'll need to decide how often you'll meet, for how many hours, and over what period of time. You may want to establish some 'ground rules' – such as respecting confidentiality and not putting each other down. You will also need to decide what to do in your groups and may find the following suggestions useful:

- **Personal sharing:** *each person in the group has an opportunity to talk about their feelings and experiences in relation to a particular issue – ogling women, rage or work, for example.*

- **Exploring group dynamics:** *talking about the relationships and roles within the group. Do you compete with each other? Does anyone take control? How does it feel to be in a group of men? How easy is it to express anger towards another group member?*

- **Creative activities:** *using painting, sculpting, drama, poetry or music as a way of exploring your masculinity. Try making a mask, for instance, of your inner Arnie; or use role-playing to explore how you relate to women.*

- **Campaigning:** *undertaking activities that challenge traditional sex roles – tackling sexual harassment at work or campaigning for better health services for men, for example.*

- **Discussions:** *talking in a less personal and more abstract way about issues of masculinity (although watch out, it's easy for intellectual debate quickly to dominate the group).*

- **Checking in/out:** *sharing time at the beginning or end of the group just to talk about how you're feeling at the moment or what's currently significant in your life.*

Emotions – we can't live with them and we can't live without them. They're scary, unpredictable and uncomfortable. They're also exciting, challenging and often simply wonderful. We can try to repress them yet we know they're always there, ready to surface as soon as we let down our guard. We can understand, value and even enjoy our emotions far more, however, once we allow ourselves to take the risk of talking about and expressing them. Acknowledging and accepting our feelings is an essential first step to better self-knowledge, and sharing them is central to getting closer to others. Of course, real men must always be as cold, hard and unfeeling as a baseball bat; they are not distracted from their mission by feelings – falling in love, a touch of the blues, guilt or fear would only get in the way. But complete men are able to combine, and balance, the strength and resilience of the traditional man with a new vulnerability and sensitivity. It's an attractive, if not irresistible, possibility.

# relationships:
# the intimate man

## head over heels

For a lot of women, it's the 'big L'. For a lot of men, it's the point when we want to slouch off for a drink or go to sleep. Talking about 'lurve' doesn't seem to come very high on the male agenda. Many of us are not very good at it. When women say things like, 'I do love you, but I'm not *in* love with you', a lot of us are left wondering what the hell they're talking about. Sex we can handle. Marriage and divorce we can just about get a grip on. But romance ... well, it's all a bit soppy, isn't it?

In a way, it's not surprising that many of us have this attitude. After all, while girls were running around the playground trying to persuade us to play kiss chase, most of us were more interested in kicking a ball or kicking each other. Barbie and Ken may have taught girls the lessons of love, but Lego bricks and tubs of slime did little for our knowledge of passion. When most of us were at school, anything that had the faintest whiff of love was decidedly 'girlie', and we may still feel a shudder of embarrassment when the topic comes up.

But there's more to it than that. As men, we often have a

fear of falling in love because we don't like to fall anywhere – we simply don't like to let go and lose control. When we love someone, it can feel as if we've allowed them to have influence over our feelings and behaviour. Suddenly, we find ourselves buying expensive, silk boxer shorts and putting the toilet seat down after we've used it. We sit helplessly by the phone, waiting for our lover to ring and reassure us that she hasn't met someone new that day. We might even feel lonely when she's not around, happy at the thought of seeing her, excited when we're with her. We need her to make our lives fulfilled, and that sense of dependency can be pretty damn scary.

## stand back

Some men's reluctance to fall in love is also rooted in one of the most pervasive characteristics of men in relationships – a fear of intimacy. To be intimate with someone requires opening up, being honest about our inadequacies and vulnerabilities. Many of us, however, are scared to reveal our soft underbelly. We think that if we show people how we really are, they'll lose respect for us as a man. We feel that to be loved, we have to build a wall around ourselves, making us appear strong and powerful. Ironically, we often end up doing precisely the opposite of what many women say they want.

Because many of us are so afraid of revealing our 'inner selves', we can often feel uncomfortable and embarrassed when people start asking us about our personal lives. We often **49** find it easier to talk about abstract or impersonal things – such as sport, cars or politics – instead of our feelings and personal experiences. In this way we keep people at an arm's length, never really getting to know them or allowing them to know us.

For some of us, however, it's not so much that we don't want to talk personally, it's more that we don't know how. Talking intimately is like any language, it's something we learn and, for many of us, it's about as hard as speaking Icelandic. But it's also something that we can become fluent in. The more we start talking honestly about ourselves – weaknesses as well as strengths – the easier it becomes. A good teacher can help, and often a partner skilled in the language of intimacy can point us in the right direction. We might think talking about our feelings sounds 'woosie', but few women or men listening to us will actually think, 'What a jerk!'

## commitmentphobia

Many men feel torn between believing they 'ought' to be 'playing the field' – in other words, having as many lovers as possible – and feeling they 'ought' to be in a steady relationship. Even though, as we get older, we may feel that it's time to settle down, many of us are still scared to commit ourselves. It's an age-old problem: she wants kids, we want a trip to Nepal; she wants us to buy a house together, we're happy in our small rented apartment; she wants to get married, we want to get drunk. The growing independence of women has changed some of these attitudes to relationships, but not that much – men's faltering commitment is still the major complaint of many women.

Even when we do commit to a serious relationship, it's often partially rather than fully. Our aversion to dependence can lead to a fear of giving ourselves entirely; we prefer instead to keep one foot inside and one foot outside the relationship – the perfect position for a quick getaway. Keeping an eye out for other women, immersing ourselves in our work and not spending time with our partner can all be ways in which we hold back from a full, 100 per cent commitment.

For many of us, a reluctance to commit ourselves also stems from a fear of being tied down. Many men hang on to romantic fantasies of roaming the earth armed with nothing more than a pair of Levi's and a packet of condoms. And it's not so much that we *want* to sleep with a thousand women (although a GQ magazine survey of 1,000 men did find that one third thought it acceptable for a man in an established relationship to sleep with someone else), it's more that we want to have the *choice* to be able to. As men, we're used to having a substantial degree of freedom in our lives, and we'd hate to see it curtailed.

Fear of commitment may go back to the early mother/son relationship. Because women are generally assigned the role of child-rearer, our mother was probably the person who brought us up. Consequently, many of us were deeply connected to her – without fear, reservation or barriers. She was the person we turned to when we needed warmth or loving. Hers was the lap 51 we sat on when we were sad or afraid. As we grew up, however, we were expected to break away from our mothers. We were told to stop being 'a mummy's boy' and to free ourselves from her 'apron strings'. Our mum knew – and we soon learnt – that if we were seen kissing her goodbye at the school gates, serious teasing was bound to follow.

Awarely or not, we pulled away from her – a process that was almost certainly difficult as well as traumatic. If we carry this scar into adult life, it can leave us with a feeling that deep relationships are not going to last and will only lead to hurt. The fear of going through the pain we felt when we separated from our mother can stop us wanting to risk committing ourselves again. Many men are also left with a deep fear of rejection by women, and you don't need to be Sigmund Freud to realize that one of the easiest ways to avoid being rejected is to do the rejecting.

The mother/son relationship can affect men's commitment to women in another way. While we may have been deeply in love with our mother and wanted to stay close to her, there was probably part of us that actually wanted to break free from her grasp, so we could establish our independence and start to explore the world around us. At times, her love and concern for us could have felt smothering. We may well have resented it when she told us, 'No, you can't play in the middle of the road,' or 'You really shouldn't fiddle with your penis in public.' As adults, if we 'project' this dynamic onto other women, we can end up seeing a female partner as

the person who's always trying to put clamps on what

we're doing. We'll see her as parental and overbearing, rather than realizing that she's simply like us, a person with needs of their own.

With all these fears, it isn't that easy for many of us to let go, fall in love or commit ourselves to relationships. The temptation is always to sit on the sidelines and to focus our energies on something that seems less threatening – driving fast or working hard, for example. But before doing that, we should take a few moments to reflect on the importance and value of love, intimacy and commitment. Knowing that you care deeply for someone – and that they also care deeply about you – is a profound, life-changing experience. It makes the world seem a much more secure, welcoming, happier and delightful place. It's true that we can end up getting hurt – sometimes very painfully – but we have to weigh a life of certainty and safety against one of passion and emotion. It's worth remembering, too, that commitment is about intimacy, not dependency. The committed man doesn't have to surrender his own identity; in fact, some psychologists say that the more someone retains their sense of self, the deeper their commitment, and intimacy, can be.

## just like a woman

Some men seem to think that so long as they don't open doors for women, then they can't be sexist. If that were true, the world would be a far happier place. Unfortunately it isn't. Sexism – oppressive behaviour towards women on the basis    53 of their sex alone – operates on two levels. Most obviously, there is conscious sexism, where men make a deliberate effort to impede the lives of women. More subtly, there's the kind of sexism where we automatically make negative assumptions about women. While many men these days may not be guilty of the first type of sexism, few of us can honestly claim that we're not perpetrators of the second. From the moment we're born, we're exposed to stereotypes about women, and not to have taken these on board would have required a considerable feat of mental engineering.

Women can, of course, also hold prejudiced stereotypes about men, but because of men's greater political, economic and social power, we've a far greater ability to impose our prejudices on the lives of females. As the equation goes, 'Oppression equals prejudice *plus* power.' Because we hold most of the keys to economic power, for instance, we can stop women climbing the office hierarchy if we believe that women are not as good at work as men. Women, on the other hand, have far fewer ways to make their stereotypes about men directly affect our lives. Men are certainly repressed – if they weren't there'd be no need for this book – but this tends to be something we do to ourselves and each other rather than something externally imposed.

It's become fashionable recently to claim that the 'sex war' is over and that women and men are now equal. While women's lot has undoubtedly improved in the last 30 years, the facts suggest that women are still significantly disadvantaged. Women's average earnings are some two-thirds of men's, for example, and relatively few have made it into senior management positions. The vast majority of politicians, judges and surgeons are men. Women are much more likely to be in low-paid, part-time or clerical work and to be responsible for most unpaid domestic labour, including childcare. Most of us would still probably be surprised, and (if we're honest) perhaps a bit worried too, if we discovered that our airline pilot or car mechanic was a woman.

While most of us are largely unaware of our sexism, some men are conscious of their attitudes and behaviour and feel very guilty about it; sometimes they also feel guilty about other men's sexism. But experience suggests that this guilt doesn't help us change very much. If we feel guilty about being sexist, we may end up pretending – to ourselves and others, especially women – that we've changed, even though we continue to have thoughts and feelings which are little different from most other men's. And, even though we try to deny it, those thoughts and feelings can still affect our behaviour. However, if we can see our sexism as a part of growing up male, the process of acknowledging it then becomes less fraught. That doesn't mean we should start jumping around and celebrating the fact that we're sexist – not feeling guilty doesn't mean we can't take responsibility for tackling sexist behaviour. But it's only when we allow ourselves to be fully aware of our sexism that we can really start to tackle it.

So how does sexism affect men's relationships with women? Put simply, if how we relate to someone is based on assumptions about them then we're not actually relating to them as 55 an individual. We don't give them a chance to be who they want to be, and we don't give ourselves a chance to see their true qualities. For instance, one of the most common assumptions many of us make about women is that they're less intelligent, rational and capable than us at certain tasks. If our doctor is a woman, for instance, we might be less inclined to take her advice or perhaps even to visit her again. Alternatively, we may not take seriously what women say in discussions; we'll assume their arguments are weak or frivolous before we've even heard them. If we're the manager of a company, we may assume that a woman will not be as good at a job as a man, and consequently hire a man whose abilities are actually inferior. As a result of this, women are often put in a position where they have to work twice as hard as men to prove that they are half as good.

## carry on nurse

One of the most common stereotypes men have about women is to see them as nurturers, the people who provide us with love and support. We can expect to be cared for in several ways. We might assume, for instance, that it's a woman's role to clean the flat, change the bedsheets and cook for us; or we might see her as being there to provide us with sexual pleasure rather than having needs of her own; or we might expect her to sort out any difficulties that come up in our relationship. And while it's true that some men often find

it hard to talk intimately with women, they do still turn to them for emotional support, perhaps when things get tough at work or when they're ill.

To a large extent, this attitude towards women can probably be traced back to our relationship with our mother. As we have already seen, she looked after us (in most cases), and many of us expect all subsequent women to do much the same. So we may take on the role of the irresponsible little boy – sneaking off to a bar and griping about having to clean the bath – while she feels forced into the mothering role, nagging us to come home at a reasonable time and to make an equal contribution to domestic chores. We may be adult and responsible at work, but the moment we get home we're reduced to the maturity of a ten-year-old.

At the same time, however, if we see women as nurturers and mother-figures, we may also desperately want to win their unqualified approval. After all, there's little that can seem more attractive than the love and warmth a woman can give us. So some men put women on a pedestal, always doing things to please them and trying hard not to get angry or irritated with them. Few women, however, really appreciate this kind of treatment. Having someone following you around like a wide-eyed puppy dog can be as annoying as having someone barking like a pit bull terrier. Moreover, men who suppress their negative feelings towards women often build up hidden resentments. So stereotypes, even when they seem positive, can still have a negative effect.

## isn't she lovely?

Imagine you're dating Cindy Crawford. Whenever you go out for a pizza, or a drink and a game of darts, Cindy's there on your arm. And everybody – especially your mates – knows that, afterwards, she'll be going home with you for a long night of passionate lovemaking. How would that feel? Probably pretty scary, especially if you're not quite sure why she's going out with you in the first place. But you might also feel pretty pleased with yourself. After all, if Cindy fancies you it must mean you're a very special kind of guy. It tells the world that you're either very rich, very powerful or that there's not much room to spare in your Y-fronts.

A relationship with Cindy might be an appealing prospect, but it could be revealing another sexist attitude – seeing women as little more than vehicles for our own male ego. Like mediaeval knights, we try to win the hand of the beautiful princess to show the world what a man we are and that we can vanquish the other knights. In this scenario, the only part of the woman we're really interested in is her physical attractiveness – not because it makes her more intelligent, a nicer person or even better in bed, but because the more desirable she is, the bigger the prize. In this way, we reduce women to the level of objects.

You might think only a few men actually view women this way. But you'd be wrong. When opinion pollsters MORI asked 800 middle-class men to describe their 'ideal woman', 82 per cent said a good figure was important, 78 per cent mentioned her face, 61 per cent her legs and eyes, 56 per cent her breasts and bottom. The top-scoring non-physical attributes were humour and wit, mentioned by 71 per cent; intelligence came next with 56 per cent. Men's tendency to value women on the basis of their sexual desirability is also reflected in American research, which shows that exposure to pornography centrefolds makes men feel that their real-life partners are of lower individual worth and that they are less in love with them.

The implications of all this for women should be obvious, but there are also many consequences for men. If we choose to have relationships with women on the basis of their looks, then we might end up spending years with a stunner who we're not actually happy with. At the same time, we can miss out on a relationship with someone we like, just because we don't fancy them. That's not to say that we should feel obliged to go out with anyone regardless of their looks, but there is another option – friendship. Many of us, because we only see women as potential trophies, forget the possibility of developing intimate friendships with women on a non-sexual basis.

## re-viewing women

A good way of looking at our attitudes to women is to think about the kinds of stereotypes we have about them. Try a very simple but useful exercise: write down all the adjectives that you associate with the word 'female'.

When a group of men and women were asked this question by a psychologist, they came up with the following (in alphabetical order): affected, affectionate, appreciative, **59**

attractive, charming, complaining, dependent, dreary, emotional, excitable, feminine, fickle, flirtatious, frivolous, fussy,
gentle, highly strung, meek, mild, prudish, rattle-brained, sensitive, sentimental, soft-hearted, sophisticated, submissive, talka-
tive, weak, whiny.

Maybe your list contains some of the same words; undoubtedly you will also have some that are different. However, what
many people find most surprising about this exercise is how
easy it is to churn out a list of common assumptions about the
way women are.

Once we've looked at our stereotypes of women, we can
then begin to think about how this affects our behaviour
towards them and start to re-evaluate it. This will not be easy,
of course, especially if we've been behaving in the same way
for years. But we can make a start. For instance, one common
male habit is to interrupt women when they're talking because
we believe, consciously or not, that what we have to say is
more interesting and important. Once we become aware of
doing this, we can then make choices about how we listen.

As well as tackling our own prejudices, it's also useful for us
to think about ways to challenge sexism on a wider level. After
all, stereotypes don't exist in our own heads alone but are
created and reinforced through social interaction. One significant way in which men can help put an end to sexism is by
confronting it in other men – whether by actively campaigning
against domestic violence or simply not laughing when someone tells a sexist joke. This can be quite a nerve-wracking thing
to do and we may feel a bit of a nerd for saying 'I find that

really sexist', but just refusing to go along with other men's sexism can have a significant impact – it says, 'Not everyone thinks the same way as you do.' This can help encourage other men who have always seen sexism as 'normal' to re-examine their beliefs.

# lads together

Communicating with women can be difficult, however it's nothing compared to the problems some of us have with other men. Impersonal topics are OK, but it's a real struggle for many of us to talk to another man about anything bordering on the intimate. Telling another man we have a problem with, say, getting an erection, is about as likely as winning the pole vault at the next Olympics. Many of us do have some close male friends, but research consistently shows that men generally have more distant relationships than women, place less value on friendship, have less contact with friends when they really need them and tend to put more emphasis on 'doing' things together – such as going fishing, being involved in politics or working. They also tend to have fewer friends, especially as they get older. As they enter their 30s and 40s, many men lose touch with their school or university friends and develop less intimate acquaintances with men from work, the pub or sports clubs. Some men even find that the only men they spend time with are the husbands of their partner's friends.

One American study looked at the communication styles of

men and women in their 20s and 30s. The subjects were asked what they talked about with their best friends and how they related to each other. The men talked mainly about topical issues: work, movies, sport. The women talked about these issues too, but they were also just as likely to discuss personal problems and their relationship with each other. Psychologists have found the typical male/male relationship to be in place even by adolescence, with less intimacy in male/male friendships compared to female/female ones.

However, if we are able to talk intimately and emotionally with other men, we've several advantages going for us. For a start, we've the potential to relate far better to each other's experience. Secondly, if we're having problems in a relationship with a woman, it's important that there's someone other than our partner to turn to for help. Some men find themselves totally isolated during relationship difficulties, while their partners are surrounded by a network of close friends. Finally, we relieve women of some of the burden of being our emotional caretakers.

## may the best man win

What do you think when you first meet another man? You might notice that he's got hairy nostrils or dandruff, but you'll probably quickly – and often quite automatically – run through a mental checklist to see how he compares to you. Is he stronger and tougher? Taller, shorter, balder, better looking? Is he dressed more expensively and fashionably? Is he funnier, more charming, more intelligent? Could he be better at his job? When we first encounter other men we often see them as competitors rather than colleagues or potential friends – we're scared that we won't be respected unless we're as manly as them.

Most competition between males, however, tends to be fairly subtle. After all, we don't want to look as if we're too desperate to prove a point. So if we're trying to match another man in the virility stakes, we're unlikely to climb on to a table and start jerking ourselves off. Instead, we might try to win women's affection by putting him down in female company, or impressing women with how much of an intelligent, humorous or new man we are. Sometimes, even *we* are not aware of just how competitive we're being. All that's felt is a vague discomfort and jealousy when another man appears to be doing better than us, and a certain satisfaction when we know we're doing alright.

Competition can often be a significant feature in male/male conversation. Mickey-taking and banter can be entertaining, but at times they reflect a hidden power struggle. Competition also stops men talking intimately with each other and sharing their fears and weaknesses. If we don't want to feel inferior to another man, we're unlikely to start telling him about our relationship problems or our misery at work. Instead, like any good soldier, we'll put up defences to ensure that he doesn't find our weak spots. After all, if he's the enemy, how can he be trusted? For all we know, he could take our secrets and use them against us.

63

Competition can also stop us from developing an ability to empathize with other men. If we're worried about failure, our attention will be focused on trying to make ourselves look good rather than on what the other person is telling us about their life. We'll find it difficult to concentrate on getting inside the other man's head and understanding him. Moreover, rather than empathizing with his pain or feeling pleased when he does well, part of us may feel relieved when he fails and disappointed when he succeeds. After all, the worse other men do in their lives, the better it can make us feel about our own.

Competition often begins at an early age, especially with our dads. Whether or not Freud was right about the Oedipus complex – in which the son competes with his father to win the love of his mother – fathers may well feel some sense of threat from a son growing up to be bigger and tougher than them. At school, too, there's also a greater emphasis on competition among boys. While girls tend to play 'communicating' games such as hand-clapping or skipping, boys' games tend to be about winning, overpowering and 'killing'. Sports at school also often reinforce a boy's competitive attitude. We learn that the world is divided into winners and losers – and nobody loves a loser.

That's not to say that *all* competition is inherently wrong – it can be immensely enjoyable and learning to accept both victory and defeat can be a useful way of coming to terms with the ups-and-downs of life. What's important is for us to have the capacity to enjoy both intimacy *and* competition.

If we're feeling competitive with another man, one thing

we're unlikely to do is to start complimenting him – even if we secretly think he's doing well. Criticizing him is of course a lot easier, but this can lead to a vicious circle. We put him down, so he feels inadequate about his masculinity, which motivates him to return the favour by putting us down, which then makes us want to put him down even more. If we were instead more honest about his achievements, it could well give him a more secure sense of identity, and he might then feel less afraid of being positive about us.

Building up more intimate male relationships, either with current or new friends, is rarely an easy process. It requires taking some risks – talking about our emotions, our vulner-abilities or even our feelings towards our friend – though there's no need to spill our guts on the first evening. We might get further, moreover, with someone who's also interested in developing closer male friendships. Expecting a man like Clint Eastwood to become our bosom buddy overnight may not be too realistic – especially if we've just tried spending four hours revealing all about our penile warts.

## 'i'm no poof'

'Poof', 'queer', 'fag', 'nancy boy' – we have a lot of insults for a man who has sex with another man. Being a gay man completely disqualifies us from being a real man. Not surprisingly, then, to identify publicly as a homosexual is to open ourselves up to ridicule, hatred, physical threats and legal discrimination. (We still can't have legal sex with another man until we're 18 and there are no laws tackling anti-gay discrimination in the workplace.) Even for those of us who are not gay, the taboos around homosexuality are so strong that they can stop us doing anything which might be considered 'poofy'.

When it comes to physical contact between men, this can cause particular problems. While many straight men kiss women as a greeting, few of us feel as comfortable kissing another man. Men rarely hold hands, cuddle or walk around arm in arm – unless they're drunk – and few of us would feel OK about sleeping in the same bed as another man, even if he was our best friend. When we do brush against another man accidentally, we often shudder with embarrassment and apologize profusely. Even straight men who've developed the ability to hug other men tend to give them the so-called 'A-frame hug', with shoulders together but crotches at least a metre apart. All this physical distance between straight men comes about because we're either afraid of looking like we're 'coming on' to the other man, or else fear he's 'coming on' to us. Homophobia – the fear of homosexuality – also makes it more difficult for straight men to get emotionally close to each other.

Many false assumptions are made about gay men. We may believe, for instance, that being gay is a kind of mental illness. We may fear that every gay man we meet wants to get us into bed. We may confuse homosexuality and transvestism and assume that gay men are more interested in dressing up in frocks than spending an evening at the movies. We may even think that all gay men are HIV positive or child abusers.

Just as sexism affects our relationships with women, so homophobia impairs our relationships with gay men – particularly our ability to develop close and intimate relationships. The more aware we are of our assumptions, however, the more we can challenge them. If the words 'gay' or 'homosexual' trigger a series of stereotypical thoughts or images, we can think about what they are and where they might have come from. Perhaps they stem from what we heard our parents say, or from jibes and put-downs in the school playground. Understanding our homophobia can not only improve our relationship with gay men but also our relationship with straight men.

While 6–10 per cent of the population is believed to be gay, psychologists believe that many more men probably have, or have had, some sexual feelings towards other men. In this sense, 'gay' and 'straight' are not rigidly defined identities but the end points of a continuum along which we all lie. However, because of the prejudice attached to homosexuality, many men suppress their sexual feelings towards other men. This can lead to deep feelings of guilt and shame, and men who repress their bisexuality or homosexuality can end up living their lives denying their true feelings. It may be that some men deal with the fear of their own gayness by 'splitting themselves off' from it and vigorously condemning homosexuality whenever they see it in others. It can be hard for us to know whether we're affected by this psychological process. But we could ask ourselves how our sexuality might be different if we were free from the pressures, constraints and fears that society imposes on all of us. It could help to think back to our adolescence to see if we can recall any feelings of sexual desire for other males and how we felt about these feelings.

# hearing aid

One problem some of us may have in any relationship is that we're poor listeners. We spend most of the time in a discussion speaking in lectures rather than two-way conversation, keeping the topic of the discussion on *our* lives and *our* interests, and switching off when the other person starts to talk about themselves. Though we may not be aware that we behave like this – and often we won't want to admit it to ourselves – people around us may well have noticed. Being a bad listener is like having bad breath, it stops people from wanting to get to know us. And if we never listen to the lives of others, we're unlikely to get to know them. We generally assume that the way to 'give' in a conversation is by talking and 'informing' others, but the opposite is often true: we also give by simply listening and affirming the other person.

If we want to know whether we're a good listener or not, we could try calculating roughly what percentage of time in conversations we tend to spend talking. Do we speak and listen in equal amounts, or does one vastly outweigh the other? Sometimes it's difficult for us to judge for ourselves, so we might want to ask a friend to time it for us when we're not noticing; or simply ask a friend how much they think we talk.

Discovering that we talk too much can be the first step on

the route to becoming a better listener. Alternatively, we may realize that we talk much less than others in conversation. But this doesn't necessarily mean that we are listening. It could be that we're focused on our own shyness or are resenting just how much the other person is talking.

One exercise that might help us learn to listen better is to spend time with a friend taking turns just quietly listening to each other. We can agree on an amount of time, say five minutes, and then just listen to that person talking without interrupting. Then we can swop around. This may sound rather rigid, but we don't have to converse like this for the rest of our lives.

## sorting out the mess

It's often said that in tenpin bowling the difference between a good player and a bad player is not how many strikes they get (knocking down all ten pins), but how good they are at picking up the spares (the pins left after the first bowl). The same could be said for relationships: a good relationship is not necessarily measured by how perfectly it begins, but by how well we deal with the difficulties that arise. In every relationship – with a lover, friend or colleague – problems are bound to arise; these can either be seen as an obstacle to be avoided or as a challenge which can help to move the relationship on.

Unfortunately, many of us believe that if we don't get all the pins down the first time, we should just give up and walk away. Men are notoriously bad at dealing with relationship difficulties – often they're more inclined to avoid them than to confront them head-on. Sometimes that's because we don't want to admit that there's anything wrong. Sometimes it's because we can't deal with the powerful emotions that talking about relationships can bring up. Sometimes we're quite happy with what we've got and we've no desire for change. And, of course, the fact that many of us don't know the language of intimacy doesn't make discussing relationship difficulties any easier.

It's often said that there are three main negotiating styles: aggressive, manipulative and assertive. Traditionally, men have plumped for the first style. However, when we're aggressive, we're actually not really negotiating at all – we're trying to impose what we want without giving the other person space to air their needs. If, for instance, we're sick of our partner talking about her ex-boyfriend, we might shout at her, 'Why the hell can't you just shut up about him?' But behaving in such a way – apart from being threatening – rarely gets us what we want. The other person may do things our way for a while, but it's more out of fear than because they want to. Our girlfriend may shut up about her 'ex', but she'll resent us for it, and she'll probably try to hurt us in other ways to get her own back.

A lot of men, however, are not 'into' anger. We're scared of being aggressive, of telling people what our needs are. So instead of explicitly stating what we want, we try to get our needs met indirectly – a technique known as manipulative or 'passive-aggressive'. So when our girlfriend starts talking about her ex, we don't shout at her. Instead we might start sulking (punishing her with our silence), or else go on about how useless we are (punishing her with guilt). Effectively we're still trying to get her to shut up about her old lover; we're just trying to hide what we're doing. Manipulation can be a lot more effective than aggression, but it's a convoluted way of getting what we want. It also confuses both the other person and ourselves about what our real needs are and so can lead to even larger problems.

One of the main reasons why we often act manipulatively is that we feel guilty about having needs. We might think it's wrong for us to want to silence our girlfriend or to be jealous, and so we try to hide our real feelings. Men who go along with the view that 'all men are bastards' may feel particularly guilty about having any needs at all. However, there are two important things to remember. First, whether we like it or not, we all have needs, and if we try to repress them, we'll just try to get them met in covert ways. Secondly, we can only change those things we acknowledge, so it's only once we face up to our jealousy of our partner's ex and talk about it that we can begin to sort out what's really going on.

Rather than being aggressive or manipulative, it's often far better to be assertive. Essentially this is just a matter of being honest. All we have to do is state clearly and straightforwardly what we want and how we're feeling. So we might say, 'I wish you wouldn't always talk about your ex-boyfriend. It makes me feel really upset.' Of course, this can sometimes be extremely difficult to do – we may feel guilty, scared that the other person will hate us, afraid of hurting the other person or 71 that we're making a fuss about nothing. However, until we take the risk and explicitly state what we want, we're unlikely to get our needs met.

The more honest we can be about our feelings, the more likely we'll be able to reach a positive outcome. So we may want to spend some time really thinking about what's going on inside our head. It may be, for instance, that the mention of our lover's ex makes us feel uncomfortable because we're afraid that she wants to go back to him. If that's the case, then it would be a lot more useful asking our lover about her feelings towards him rather than just asking her not to mention him any more. Moreover, if the other person can see what we're really feeling, they're much more likely to respond in the way we want them too. If they can see that we're upset or hurt, they may try to support us or change their behaviour; if they just think we're being pushy or manipulative, they're less likely to be particularly sympathetic.

Of course, it's not enough just to state our needs and leave it at that. The other person is bound to have needs too, and the chances are they want theirs met just as much as we want ours met. So we have to be prepared to listen to the other person's perspective on things, to see how they feel and the reasons why they're behaving in the way they are. In doing so, hopefully each of us can get as many of our needs met as possible. Psychologists call this a 'win/win' outcome – one where both parties get most of what they want. This is clearly preferable to the more traditional 'win/lose', or even

'lose/lose', outcomes of many relationship disputes.

Often problems in relationships can be cleared up once the real needs are brought into the light, untangled from the messy world of manipulative communications. It may be, for instance, that a woman's reason for talking about her ex-lover so much is that she is angry with her current lover for not paying her enough attention. Once we know this, we can begin to acknowledge her in the way she wants. Consequently, she's less likely to punish us by bringing up the topic of her ex. However, not all difficulties can be sorted out with such quick-fix solutions. Sometimes the needs of both parties are miles from each other. Sometimes they're mutually exclusive. It's never easy in these situations to reach the perfect compromise, but there are some tips that can help talking about the issues to be as productive as possible:

- *Try to talk about your feelings and needs rather than abstract ideas. You can argue all day about whether cooking is harder than driving the car, but saying 'I feel angry when you criticize my driving' is indisputable. There's now considerable research suggesting that men who are able to be emotionally expressive have longer-lasting and happier relationships.*
- *If things get emotionally 'heavy' or highly charged, try not to give up. Although relationships can often feel very fragile and at risk if heated things get said, the reality is that any relationship with potential will almost certainly take a lot to break up for good.*
- *Try not to 'demonize' the other person. In other words,*   **73**

don't build them up into some kind of monster as a way of reassuring yourself that you must be right. If you think to yourself, 'She's the bitchiest, most neurotic woman I've ever met', then you're likely to find it harder to see her clearly as someone who has different needs from you and is probably also upset and angry.

- Trust that the other person is telling you the truth, especially about their feelings. Try not to tell them what their experiences are or how they're feeling.

- Try to get an idea of how things look from the other person's perspective. A very productive exercise, if you can bring yourself to do it, is to 'swop' places, pretend you're the other person, and argue things from their viewpoint.

- Be aware of when you're just hanging on to your side of the argument because you want to be right. It may be painful to give in, but ultimately less damaging to a relationship than doggedly sticking to a position neither of you believes in.

- Try not to leave yourself with things you wish you'd said. The more you get out in the open, the clearer things will be at the end of the day.

- And finally, for effective negotiation you don't have to be deadpan and 'rational'. Any emotions that come up – anger, sadness, amusement, joy – are an integral part of the process.

# getting a hand

About a year ago, the pressures were building up more and more for Warren, a 43-year-old printer:

> Diane and I went through the stress of adopting a child and then I changed my job. Eventually everything just cracked. I met someone else and that was it. I just upped and moved out for three months.

The longer Warren lived apart from his family, the more he missed them, especially the children. But he and Diane couldn't find a way of sorting out their differences. Then Diane suggested relationship counselling. At first Warren was very sceptical and thought it was a waste of time, plus: 'I didn't want anyone telling me how I should run my life.' But it did help:

> The counsellor opened my eyes to things and I really wanted to know the deep-down cause of my behaviour. We spent a lot of time talking about the fact that I'd been an only child – I'd never really thought about that before. I was shocked to realize how selfish I was and how I ran away from problems rather than face up to them. I never saw counselling as the universal panacea, I just saw it as somewhere I could talk and make my own decisions. It also coaxed me along the right path. Going to counselling was the second best thing I ever did – the first was coming back to Diane. And, without the counselling, I don't think we'd be back together again now.

Sometimes relationships do get into difficulties which we can't sort out for ourselves. It may be impossible to discuss a problem without it always turning into an argument; we or our partner may have totally withdrawn emotionally; or the issues may just be too painful for us to find a way through them. In these situations, having a third person present can be an invaluable aid. It can create a safer environment and provide a more objective standpoint from which to evaluate the relationship. Couples can either attend together, or with only one partner going if the other doesn't want to.

The purpose of relationship counselling isn't necessarily to keep a relationship going but to find the solution that is most appropriate for both people. If the best outcome at the end of the day is separation, counselling tries to help this happen with a minimum of bitterness and with an opportunity to learn for the future. Either way, relationship counselling isn't easy or quick – problems can be deep-seated and take a long time to resolve.

Many men feel inhibited about going to see a professional counsellor. We may see it as an admission that we're unable to sort out the problems in the relationship on our own or that we can no longer cope. And, to some extent, visiting a professional is an acknowledgement that we're no longer able to deal with what's going on. However, the increasing number of men who are attending relationship counselling suggests that we are beginning to place our happiness and our relationships before our inner Arnie.

A real man doesn't have a problem with relationships, mainly because he doesn't have any. He's a loner who trusts no-one. Take Superman. He can't get really close to his friend Lois Lane because he feels he can't reveal the single most important detail of his life (his double identity). Even when he meets up with other super-heroes, they spend all their time beating super-villains rather than chilling out with a beer and discussing the heavy burden of responsibility they carry for saving humanity.

However, it's virtually impossible to flourish and develop as a man without a wide variety of intimate and loving relationships with both women and other men. That closeness enables us to share ourselves and learn about others, but with out giving up our own needs or identity. This requires honesty, openness and being assertive while learning to see women without the stereotypes of sexism and men without the fear of homosexuality. If we can develop better relationships with both men and women, we'll be well on our way to being complete men.

# sex:
# the sensual man

## performing zeal

It's been a passionate night of lovemaking. You reach for a cigarette, a mug of herbal tea or whatever takes your fancy. 'Darling,' you say, 'how was that for you?'

'To be honest,' she replies, 'boring, unadventurous and irritating. You didn't go down on me, you half squashed me to death, and you didn't even bother finding out whether I'd come or not!'

How would that make you feel? The answer is probably something like 'terrible', 'gut-wrenched' or 'humiliated'. It's not as if someone's just told you you've got a lousy golf swing or your car needs a paint job. Criticism of our sexual virility hits us right where it hurts – our identity as a man. Real men, so we've been told, are maestros between the sheets. They can unclip a woman's bra straps without spending 20 minutes trying to work out whether the catch is on the front or the back; they can find her clitoris without fumbling; and they can bring her to a moaning, shuddering orgasm just by unzipping their trousers.

Of course, the real man is not only technically perfect, he also makes love like a Martini – any time, any place, anywhere. Whether he's in the middle of the park or on the back seat of a bus, he doesn't say, 'Look, this is really embarrassing, can we stop it.' Instead he's ever-prepared with an everlasting erection, a 'stiffy' that refuses to wilt even after the seventh time that night. 'Yes honey,' he says, 'of course I want more. Let's keep doing it.'

As well as being the ultimate sex machine, a lot of us feel we should be walking copies of *The Good Sex Guide*. We can easily believe good sex is largely a matter of technique and that, to be a great lover, we must know about everything from position 209 of the *Kama Sutra* to the mysteries of the G-spot. After all, isn't that what women expect?

The problem is, while real men might be super-studs with PhDs in sexology, most of us don't actually come close. And if we feel we're sexual failures unless we live up to the image of the sex god, then we're putting ourselves under an inordinate amount of pressure. Instead of sex being an opportunity for us to experience intimacy with another person, or just the chance to have fun, it can become a deeply anxiety-ridden affair, where the worry of 'Am I Mr Perfect-in-bed?' detracts from the physical and emotional pleasures of making love. When we're striving hard to be good between the sheets, it's almost impossible to let go and fully immerse ourselves in the act of sex. To give our 'best' performance, we feel we must stay in control throughout.

So the irony is that performance-anxiety, if anything, makes **79** for poorer lovemaking. Apart from the fact that our tension may well be obvious and prevent our lover from relaxing, a mind focused on performance isn't going to be very aware of the fact that there's another person in the bed. This can make a woman feel we're distant and disconnected. Moreover, even if we could become technically perfect, sex is about two people being together, not about one person and a sex machine. If our partner wanted purely physical stimulation, she'd probably go for a vibrator.

It's also worth remembering that sexual knowledge is something we learn, not something we're born with and, if we expect to know it all straight away, we're going to be in for a nasty shock and a lot of humiliation. In fact, claiming to know it all actually stops us from finding out more, because we're either too afraid to ask or too freaked out to listen when someone comments on our sexual behaviour. Flying off into fits of suicidal despair when a woman informs us that we're trying to stick our penis up her anus not her vagina (when it's her vagina we're aiming for) does not actually help us do it right the next time. Listening to what she has to say and learning from her, however, provides a much better chance of developing our sexual awareness.

## the casanova complex

Remember the man with the gold medallion, the hairy chest and a string of girlfriends as long as his penis? These days, he may be about as fashionable as flared trousers and six-inch stacks, but there's still a little Medallion Man sitting on most men's shoulders whispering, 'Go on … try to get her into bed … see how many women you can sleep with.' And every time we score, the inner Medallion Man gives us a slap on the back and says, 'Well done – and who's next?'

Sleeping around undoubtedly makes many of us feel good – we enjoy the conquest of new flesh in much the same way as an explorer loves to conquer new lands. We may enjoy the sex, we may even like our partner, but if we can make a woman succumb, it makes us feel powerful, virile, attractive and desirable. The next day, we walk out of the bedroom with a proud, taut body, bursting at the seams with manhood.

For some men, sex can become a virtual addiction, just like nicotine or alcohol. Sex addiction has many possible causes, but often what it comes down to is that men feel unloved and uncared for and use sex as a way of trying to get close to people. Strangely, it's often easier to have sex than it is to talk and share openly, honestly and intimately. And this can be just as true for the man who feels a compulsive need to have sex with one partner as the man who has sex with hundreds. Men whose sexual behaviour is motivated in this way often eventually realize that they never really feel satisfied or fulfilled, no matter how many women they sleep with or how often they have sex. They find they have to discover other, longer-lasting ways of meeting their needs.

Although many men still aspire to be Casanova, the harsh reality is that most of us come nowhere near. The British National Survey of Sexual Attitudes and Lifestyles, which, in the early 90s, looked in detail at the behaviour of over 8,000 men aged 16–59, found that 21 per cent have had only one heterosexual partner and 29 per cent between two and four partners. 24 per cent have had ten or more partners, but under 2 per cent have had five or more partners in the last year. The same survey found that about one in five men aged 16–24 are still virgins, as are almost 2 per cent of all 16–59-year-olds. However, the study did find one man who claimed to have had 4,500 partners, so there may be at least one real man around after all.

The same survey suggests that we're not at it all the time either. Although it's easy to believe everyone else is shagging like bunnies, the average heterosexual of any age doesn't make love more than five times a month. The study also found that only a small number of people have sex up to 130 times a month, perhaps not surprisingly since bonking four or five times a day wouldn't leave very much time for anything else!

But for those men who are not copulating at all, even these statistics may make depressing reading. Unwanted celibacy when you're between relationships can seem bad enough, but virginity can seem an almost intolerable burden, especially as a man gets older. Virginity simply doesn't seem a desirable condition for any aspiring real man. It suggests that we're unattractive, we can't control women and we certainly can't get them into bed. The image we have of the male virgin – a wimpy, soft, mummy's boy, probably more interested in trainspotting than girls – isn't one that many men would happily aspire to.

Embarrassment about sexual inexperience can actually

make it more difficult for a man to lose his virginity. Although he may be desperate to sleep with someone, he may also be afraid that he'll be humiliated when his partner discovers he doesn't know what he's doing – especially if he's at an age where he feels his virginity should be long gone. So he either avoids any opportunities for sexual contact altogether, or else he's so nervous when the possibility comes up that he's more in a state of panic than one of sexual arousal.

The concept of virginity also puts a lot of emphasis on penetration as opposed to other sexual practices. It's as if we're only a 'proper' adult once we've 'gone all the way' – nothing else counts, even if we have a steady partner. This can make it difficult for any of us to value anything short of intercourse. The focus, especially for younger men, is on 'making fourth base' rather than enjoying what we're doing and taking it slowly and sensually.

## small is beautiful?

Most of us reckon we've come to terms with the size of our penis – by our late teens we probably know it's not going to grow any more, although we may still have strong feelings about it. As men, the size of our 'pole' can be more than just the dimension of an organ which dangles between our legs – it's a symbol of virility, manliness and self-worth. So if we consider ourselves a 'big boy', we're liable to feel proud of our penis, showing it off in the school showers or carefully manoeuvring our body to ensure that our lovers get a good eyeful. If we could, we'd probably even consider snipping it off for display on the mantelpiece.

On the other hand, a man who thinks his penis is too small may have strong feelings of shame and self-doubt. He might dart into the changing rooms after swimming so no-one can see the non-existent bulge, or always get undressed in the dark to prevent lovers from commenting on his minor member. Penis-size anxiety can, in some cases, disrupt a man's enjoyment of a sexual experience. If he's so worried that his lover's going to burst into laughter the moment she sees his penis and shout, 'Make love with that, I couldn't even pick my teeth with it!', the chances are he won't be very relaxed. For many of us, being told our penis is too small could be a profoundly humiliating experience.

As men, we compete with each other over numerous things, but the battle of the trouser bulges differs from a lot of other competition in one very dramatic way: we can go on a body-building course to strengthen our muscles, we can buy a bigger car, we can search around for a more beautiful wife, but – short of plastic surgery – it's impossible for us to get a bigger penis. It's an unchanging symbol of our masculinity. So it's no wonder that young boys watch their penises growing as anxiously as a cook watching his soufflé rising. Once it stops, we're stuck.

What adds to penis-size anxiety is the fact that many of us assume that other men's penises are bigger than they actually are. Straight men have few opportunities to observe other men's penises (especially erect ones). Since the only ones we tend to know about are the 10-inch monsters depicted in pornography, it's hardly surprising that we can end up feeling inadequate. After all, compared to King Dong's 'stonker', most of us are still playing hunt the acorn. In fact, the average penis is a much more modest 6 inches long when erect, and 90 per cent of penises fall 1 inch either side of this. To get a better idea of the actual size of your organ, try looking at it sideways on in a mirror; peering down can give a highly misleading perspective.

Although it's clearly a nonsense to value ourselves by the length of our penis, before we rejoice and proclaim, 'Size doesn't count', it's important to listen to what women have to say. A large survey of British and German women for the sex magazine *Women Only* found that while 90 per cent felt that penis size didn't affect their orgasm, about the same proportion considered penis length and width to be 'sometimes' or 'always' important while making love. Of those women with experience of a larger than average penis (8–9 inches), 56 per cent found it more satisfying than normal. An *Arena/New Woman* survey also found that almost four in ten women thought penis size was 'vital' or 'quite important' for a fulfilling sex life.

But before digging out the ruler from the bedside cabinet, it's important to remember that when women say that size does matter, they almost certainly are not saying they only admire or respect a man if he's got a big penis. To men, penis size is a matter of pride. To women, it's much more a matter of sexual pleasure. So it's not that they don't respect or enjoy sex **85** with a lightly-hung man, it's just that a bigger penis might feel nicer inside them – in the same way that some men find a tighter vagina provides a snugger fit.

# before it's time

Exactly when an ejaculation is premature is a topic of some debate among sex therapists. Indeed, one therapist discovered a man who thought he suffered from premature ejaculation because he couldn't hang on for more than 45 minutes of vigorous thrusting! But ejaculation is obviously premature if the man comes before he's walked through the front door, and it's probably premature if he starts spurting before or at the moment of penetration. Apart from that, however, it's difficult to say what's too fast. It probably makes most sense to say that an ejaculation is premature when its early appearance causes a problem in a sexual relationship.

Premature ejaculation is in fact the most common male sexual problem. Shere Hite's survey of over 7,000 American men found three-quarters were concerned that they came 'too soon'. Premature ejaculation can be caused by a variety of factors: anxiety, stress, not having learned to control ejaculation or sexual trauma. Having sex again after a long period of abstinence can also be a factor. There are no known physical causes.

Of course, real men can keep going for hours, so a man who can't hold on until his partner's had her third multiple orgasm may well feel pretty useless. Moreover, premature ejaculation can leave men's partners frustrated, hurt or even angry – high, but not exactly dry. The problem, however, is that knowing this doesn't make it any easier for men not to come too soon. Anxiety about premature ejaculation can, in fact, lead to a vicious circle where the problem seems just to get worse and worse.

The good news is that the syndrome is not inevitable. Men can learn to control their orgasms. Traditional methods of ejaculation control tend to involve bizarre mind-games – some sex manuals suggest concentrating on football scores, train timetables or even Einstein's theory of relativity. In one of his nightclub routines, Woody Allen describes how he used to think about baseball games to stem the flow. He jokes that he once became so preoccupied with a match that he didn't realize he'd finished having sex until he discovered that his partner had been in the shower for ten minutes.

The mind-game strategy, however, while sometimes effective, is no longer recommended by most sex therapists as it reduces men's involvement in the sex act, as well as their pleasure, without really tackling the root of the problem. So what can you do if you suffer from premature ejaculation? Your best bet is simply to try not to rush straight towards penetration. The more your partner is turned on before you enter her, the more quickly she could come, leaving you less time to hold on. Wearing a condom can also reduce sensitivity and hence the speed of orgasm. Another possibility is that your partner can help you with the so-called 'squeeze technique' – she squeezes the head of your penis for four seconds every few minutes **87** during sex. Over time, this can help you to learn to control your ejaculations. Many sex therapists also use so-called 'sensate focus' exercises to treat premature ejaculation (of which more later).

It also helps to remember that it's actually quite difficult for most women to orgasm while we're inside them. As any woman will tell you, when it comes to coming, the clitoris is much more important than the vagina, and it's not necessarily directly stimulated by your penis. So don't assume you simply have to hump away until something happens to her. You can always try taking your penis out and using your tongue or fingers instead.

## software problems

Keith reflects on an experience he had when he was 18:

Soon after I was inside her, I realized something wasn't right. My friends at school had told me to expect a mountain of orgasmic pleasure but I couldn't feel a foothill. I was worried and then my fear hit me like a bolt of lightening – I realized my erection had wilted. My throat became dry and my bowels felt like they were turning to water. For the first time, I understood what it meant to want the earth to open. I pulled out my willy and watched with horror as it tried to hide itself away between my legs. I felt like being sick and ran, shaking and pale, into the bathroom.

Keith was prepared to try anything:

Standing naked and cold on the tiles, I desperately tried to revive my previous virility. I tried to focus on memories of images that had aroused me when masturbating earlier that evening. I even tried applying a tub of my friend's hair gel, but to no avail. Each semi-erection I managed to coax was soon ruined by the overpowering fear of failure that was consuming me. Both physically and mentally, I was completely impotent.

Impotence – the inability to maintain an erection during sexual intercourse – is the second most common male sexual problem. Technically, the occasional erectile problem isn't impotence – that could be due to too much booze, stress or exhaustion. To be truly impotent, a man's erectile dysfunction has to last for at least several weeks. The Erectile Dysfunction Information Bureau believes that one quarter of men aged over 16 have experienced impotence and that 5 per cent of men are permanently impotent. And it gets bigger with age – the problem, that is. A major US study found that while under 10 per cent of 20–39-year-olds suffered from impotence, almost 60 per cent of 70-plus-year-olds were affected.

There are a number of causes of impotence. Some of these are physiological, including alcohol abuse, diabetes, high blood pressure, hardened arteries, the side effects of some drugs (such as beta-blockers, prescribed for high blood pressure) and low testosterone levels. However many cases of impotence **89** (perhaps 50–60 per cent) have psychological causes, such as feelings of resentment or anger towards a partner, fears about the possible consequences of intercourse (pregnancy or acquiring a sexually transmitted disease, for example) or childhood traumas such as sexual abuse. Often, the cause of impotence can also be traced back to the pressures men feel around performance. If a man is over-anxious to impress, it's possible he'll find it harder to get hard.

Whatever the causes, an inability to sustain an erection represents the ultimate sexual failure for many men. It can lead to devastating feelings of embarrassment, shame and humiliation. And if this happens, a man may be terrified that he'll go through the whole nightmare scenario again the next time he tries to make love – indeed, like premature ejaculation, impotence can easily become a vicious cycle. The harder a man tries to will his penis up, the only thing likely to rise is his anxiety level, and that means his penis will stay firmly (or not so firmly) down.

If you can't get an erection with a partner but can get one when you masturbate, when you have non-penetrative sex or during the night or on waking, the chances are that your impotence is psychologically rooted rather than physiological (although it's always a good idea for any sufferer to see a doctor for a check-up). If this is the case, trying to force an erection is the worst thing you can do. Focusing less on the penis, or its erection, can help you to let go of self-perpetuating fears, and spending more time on foreplay is one good way of doing this. Sensate focus exercises (see page 95) can also be very useful.

If the cause of impotence is physiological, there are several different and effective treatments that can improve the condition. Depending on the exact cause, these can include injections into the penis, using vacuum pumps or vascular surgery. In recent years, 'penile implants' have also been developed, particularly for cases that can't be treated in any other way. There are two types. The first is a semi-rigid silicone rod that keeps the penis erect permanently but allows it to be bent out of the way when not needed. The second type consists of two inflatable silicone cylinders inserted in the penis and connected to a small fluid-containing balloon in the abdomen with a pump in the scrotum. When the pump is squeezed, fluid flows into the cylinders and an erection results. A valve on the pump can later be used to deflate the penis. Fortunately the mechanism is not electronic, so the Sunday newspaper story about a man with a penile implant who had an erection every time his neighbour opened her electronic garage door is about as probable as finding a World War II bomber on the moon.

## phallacies

In-out, in-out, shake it all about, fall asleep – unfortunately for many of us that's about the sum total of our sex lives. Despite the anxieties some of us can have about pleasing our partners, the other side of the coin is that we can also be pretty selfish in the bedroom. Sex is centred almost exclusively on *our* genitals and *our* orgasm; while areas such as foreplay, communication, caressing and romance become relegated to the sexual dustbin. Men often rush sex, eager to get inside their partner as quickly as possible. And that's a shame, because a long, lingering build-up can be really exciting. Good sex is like a fine meal: it's possible to enjoy all the different delicacies and luxuriate in the sensual experience. We might like fast food now and again but, as we all know, one good belch and we're hungry again.

Such a penis-orientated – 'phallocentric' – approach to sex can frequently leave a female partner feeling disappointed and frustrated. If things go too quickly, by the time we're into our first snore, she may be just getting turned on. Moreover, as we've seen, women's main centre of sexual pleasure – the clitoris – is usually not directly stimulated through vaginal intercourse. So just plugging it in and hoping for the best probably won't work – at least not for her.

Part of the reason why many men have a phallocentric approach to sex may be a fear of intimacy – a perennial issue for us. Sex is, after all, an extremely personal thing to do – when we penetrate someone we're right inside them, both literally and metaphorically. And because many of us are scared of the closeness this brings, we may distance ourselves from the emotional intimacy by locating our sexual desire purely in our penis. It's as if we're saying, 'I'm not having sex, my penis is.' The penis is given a life of its own, like the Wicked Willie cartoon character. It's divorced from the rest of the body and from our feelings. Through reducing sex between two people from 'making love' to 'shagging', 'bonk-
**92** ing' or 'fucking', the sex act is depersonalized. There's no

fear of being hurt or of being out of control. It's a purely physical affair.

## the best sex ever

Whether we're worried about our sexual performance, our sexual knowledge, our virginity, our penis size, our premature ejaculation or our impotence, the way to overcome these problems may well be essentially the same – letting go of our struggle to be real men. The bottom line is that it's OK for us to not be conquistadors in bed and, the sooner we realize this, the sooner we can begin to overcome any sexual anxieties we might have.

One of the best ways men can change their point of view is by talking to women. Most of us carry a series of false assumptions about the way women want us to be. We think that unless we can come five times a night and have a penis the size of the Eiffel Tower they won't respect us. However, because women haven't been brought up with the same attitudes towards sex, often what they really think is very different. Most women, like most men, want to be sexually satisfied, but this doesn't mean that they'll necessarily think any less of a man who has some problems under the duvet. What's important is for us to find out what our partners really want, not what we think they want. That way, we're more likely to satisfy them, and also more likely to take unrealistic pressures off ourselves.

It's also invaluable to talk to other men about sex, although **93** this has to be done openly and honestly, otherwise it can do more damage than good. So choose who you talk to carefully – after all, typical male sexual boasting just heightens everyone's anxiety. The first guy says he's slept with ten women in the last year and the second one says 20 and the third says 50. So when they all go home to their bachelor pads which haven't seen a woman for the last two years, they're all thinking, 'God, have those other two really slept with so many women? I must be doing something wrong!'

Talking about sex honestly, on the other hand, can help us to realize that we're not alone with our problems, or inadequate freaks just because we don't know 35 variations of the missionary position. Once we see that others have the same fears, concerns and experiences, sex stops being such a frightening, 'unspoken' activity and becomes something we can feel much more comfortable around. We can also have a lot of fun talking about the things we love and hate about sex, and discovering that other men may feel the same way. Talking about sex can also help us to improve our sex lives by learning from one another.

It's also worth considering sensate focus exercises. These have been used, both by sex therapists and on a self-help basis, not only to tackle a wide variety of problems, but also just to improve the quality of sex. The exercises were developed in the late 1950s by William Masters and Virginia Johnson; they normally involve work with both partners and centre on removing the pressure on men to perform. Couples are initially asked to abandon direct sexual contact and are then helped to use the exercises to rediscover the pleasures of touching and being touched without the goal of penetration and orgasm. Over time, the couple move towards resuming 'normal' intercourse. Some sensate focus exercises can also be very effectively used by men – or women – on their own. The key to them all is that sex should not be rushed and that the physical pleasures should be enjoyed. In this way, they can be a invaluable tool for all men who want to develop greater sensuality. At first glance, these exercises may sound a bit … well, frankly … naff, but trying them may well be worth the risk.

- **Self-touching:** *set aside some time when you're on your own. Choose a comfortable environment – warm, soft lighting, gentle music – where you're unlikely to be disturbed. Get undressed and lie down. Put some body or massage lotion on your hand and touch and stroke every part of your body (without indulging in contortionism). Don't avoid your genitals, but try not to spend any more time on them than the other parts of your body. Try different sorts of touching – hard and gentle, circular or long strokes – keeping your attention on the skin where you are touching yourself. When you've finished, ask yourself how it felt. Was it boring or sensual? What movements or body parts did you most enjoy? Did you learn anything about yourself?*

- **Masturbating:** *start as in the above exercise, but this time go on to touch and explore your genitals more fully. Try*  95 touching your penis and testicles in different ways, perhaps including rubbing your penis on the mattress or on your stomach, or using a vibrator. Also try exploring other parts of your body such as your nipples, buttocks or anus. Keep focusing on the physical sensations rather than letting your mind wander off into fantasies. Try to make sure that you're touching your penis for at least 15 minutes before you orgasm. Again, after the exercise, reflect on how it felt.

- **Non-sexual touching with a partner:** take it in turns of ten minutes or so for you to touch your partner and for her to touch you, anywhere except the genitals or breasts. The person being caressed should focus on the physical sensation of being touched. The caresser should try to concentrate on the physical pleasure of touching the other person, again using different parts of their body to make contact. After the exercise, try to talk about it with your partner. What did you like or not like? What did you learn?

- **Sexual touching with a partner:** start with the above exercise but this time go onto the genitals, although not straight away. Try not to go straight for the orgasm either. You and your partner can bring each other to the brink many times before you finally lead them over. Again, once the exercise is over, talk about how it felt and what you learnt from the experience.

While sensate focus exercises may well be able to help us deal with a difficult sexual problem such as impotence or premature ejaculation, they can also be difficult to maintain because of the pressure to rush to intercourse. For this reason, some sex therapists believe that they should only be done under guidance. In fact, if our sexual anxiety is very high, or if we suffer chronically from other sexual problems, we might want to think about seeing a sex therapist. Sex therapy isn't about having sex with the therapist or, except very rarely, with a surrogate partner. Most therapy involves discussing our difficulties, exploring their causes and developing strategies to tackle them. It's increasingly popular and more men are willing to use it, even though it can take some courage for any man to admit to a stranger that he isn't the world's greatest lover.

## bashing the bishop

Virtually all men masturbate. Despite the best efforts of the Victorian churches and medical establishment to persuade men that it's dirty, immoral and unhealthy, over 90 per cent of men now 'beat their meat' regularly, on average 15 times a month. There can be few of us left who still believe that masturbation makes us mad, bad, bald, sterile, blind, impotent and homosexual, or causes hairs to sprout on the palms of our hands.

However, although irrational fears about masturbation have largely waned, it remains a taboo topic, tinged with shame, secrecy and the image of the dirty old man in a sleazy raincoat. **97**

You won't find many men in your local bar who'll say, 'Guess what lads, I had a really good wank last night!' That's probably because masturbating, when it comes down to it, tends to be seen as a sign of sexual failure and a poor substitute for the 'real thing'. Basically, if a man has to resort to his right (or left) hand, it signifies that he's not 'getting it' enough and that puts his 'manliness' seriously in doubt. After all, it's hard to imagine Tom Cruise with a tub of Vaseline in one hand and his penis in the other.

It's a shame this attitude is still so prevalent. Not only because it isn't true – Shere Hite's survey found that over three-quarters of men who had sex every day still masturbated at least once a week – but also because it can inhibit men from looking at some of the more interesting possibilities for masturbation. Not only can masturbating be highly enjoyable, it can also be a means of sensual and sexual exploration. And, of course, when it comes to HIV, sex doesn't come much safer.

Men tend to masturbate in the same way each time – whether it's the traditional 'hand job', the 'rubbing up and down on the sheets', or for some contortionally gifted men, 'self-fellatio' – but masturbation can be explored by trying out different techniques. If we always made love in the same position, we'd probably get bored, so why put up with it when we're making love to ourselves? We can try stimulating our penis in different ways, or touching different parts of our body (as in the sensate focus exercises), experimenting with different lubricants, or even trying a vibrator. As well as being exciting, all this self-exploration can increase our awareness of what we want when making love to someone else. It's also possible to buy an artificial vagina – even a blow-up doll complete with blinking eyes and multiple orifices – although most of these toys are about as sexy as a plastic elephant!

## dream on

Masturbation and sexual fantasy are virtually inseparable bedfellows – it's hard, indeed, to imagine one without the other. Fantasies have the potential to be one of the most exciting and liberating areas of male sexuality. As the saying goes, 'The most erotic organ we have is the one between our ears' (our brain, that is, not our nose). In the world of fantasy we can have sex in a tub of lime pickle, go down on each and every Gladiator, bump into Pamela Anderson by the cucumber counter in our local supermarket or make love to all those *Star Trek* lieutenants we used to ogle when we were younger. Through fantasy, we can explore as yet uncharted areas of our sex life, perhaps going to a prostitute, experiencing anal sex or having sex with another man. We never have to actually do what we fantasize about – that's what makes it safe and can make it fun. Unfortunately, many of us don't seem to make full use of the undoubted potential of fantasy. Maybe that's because male sex is so much focused on penetration and we've read so many pornographic magazines containing endless and virtually identical stories of unrealistic feats of bonking.

We can also experiment with sharing fantasies with our partners. Of course, she may be upset if we tell her we're fantasizing about other women – or sexual scenarios she finds offensive or even scary – so it can't be done without communication, negotiation and consent. But telling her could help bring us closer and she may even want to join us in our fantasies (and vice-versa, since our partner is just as likely to have sexual fantasies). We may also be able to create new fantasies together.

Some psychologists believe our fantasies can reveal significant information about us. For example, a man who regularly fantasizes about another woman while he's making love to his partner may feel there's something missing in his sexual activity or relationship. A man who often fantasizes about dominating a woman may well feel powerless or inferior in his relationships with either men or women. He may be angry with a woman and want some sort of revenge. A man who often fantasizes about taking women from behind could be reflecting his fear of women and his wish not to be seen by them. A man who regularly imagines women taking the sexual initiative with him could be expressing his fear of rejection by women. You might find it revealing to reflect on what your fantasies could be saying about you.

In a minority of cases, fantasies also have the potential to be quite harmful. Fantasies about oppressive sexual activities – such as rape or child abuse – may actually encourage a man to act out these out for real. Men who find themselves **100** regularly fantasizing about committing sexual offences should seriously consider going to a counsellor or sex therapist.

## soft corn

Love it or loathe it, pornography is a central feature of male sexuality. A MORI survey of 800 British men aged 18–45 found 81 per cent had read a 'soft-core' pornographic magazine at some point in their lives and 77 per cent had watched a soft-porn video. Shere Hite found that one third of men looked at pornography regularly, one fifth sometimes and one quarter infrequently. Under one fifth said they now never looked at porn. The Men and Porn Group, which works with men who use pornography compulsively, believes that some 27 million pornographic magazines are legally sold in Britain every year and that about 200 different titles are now readily available.

Arguments about the pros and cons of pornography rage on. The anti-pornography lobby argues that it encourages men to see all women as sexually available, submissive, and little more than a collection of bums, tits and vaginas – reinforcing the stereotype of women as sex objects. The anti-pornographers believe this demeaning portrayal encourages men to harass and possibly even rape women; indeed, there are now many studies which do suggest clear links between pornography and sexual violence. It's also argued that women who take part in pornography are not always the willing accomplices they appear to be. **101**

Pro-pornography campaigners, on the other hand, argue that some porn has the potential to be sexually liberating. They accuse the anti-pornography campaigners of being prudish and of dictating to the general public what they should or shouldn't be able to look at. They counter the 'porn causes rape' argument by suggesting that countries which have liberalized their pornography laws, such as Denmark, now have lower rates of sexual violence. And as for the argument that pornography degrades women, they point to the recent increase in the number of pornographic images of men. Some gay men and lesbians also oppose any anti-pornography legislation because they fear it might be used to curtail harmless homosexual images.

With the two sides of the pornography debate so polarized, it's often difficult to think clearly about the issues involved. Many of us are left confused, scared to venture an opinion or just plain bored. To break through this deadlock, one thing men may find valuable is to reflect on their own feelings and experiences of pornography. Try thinking about when you've used it most and least. What was going on in your life? Were these times when your life was going well or periods of difficulty and anxiety? Are there any particular feelings, physical or emotional, associated with your use of porn? Do you tend to nip down to the newsagent or get your mags out from their hiding place when you're feeling loved or lonely, happy or sad, relaxed or tense, loving or angry? How does your use of pornography reflect how you feel about women and do you think it's affected your attitudes towards them?

Men's responses to these questions vary widely, but many have noticed that they often use pornography as a way of coping with, or blotting out, feelings of anxiety, sadness or loneliness. It can also be a way of helping men to feel more powerful, masculine and desirable, although these feelings tend not to last for very long. Using pornography can also be related to problems in initiating and sustaining sexual relationships, fears about rejection or inhibitions about asking for sexual needs to be met.

Some men have realized that porn presents them with a pretty unrealistic image of women. Not only are the models in porn mags and videos always 'dying for it', they also have perfectly proportioned bodies, oiled skins, vaginas that are made to look as voluptuous as possible and a wealth of erotic lingerie. This can make it harder for some men to get turned on by real women who, unlike *Playboy* centre-folds, have spots, stretch marks, smells and cellulite. Moreover, pornographic models are not generally presented as having sexual needs of their own: they don't insist on an orgasm, they don't mind if you fall asleep the moment you've come and they don't expect to be rung up the next day. Pornographic sex is pretty limited too: it's almost always totally centred on physical sensations. There's no love, romance or emotional involvement and no worries about pregnancy or sexually transmitted diseases.

Pornography also presents men with unrealistic expectations of their own sexuality. Men in pornographic magazines and films are ever-willing for sex, always hung like donkeys **103** and always manage to satisfy their partners. The idea that men should be Casanovas and walking sex guides is reinforced by pornography. Given that pornography is often the first (and sometimes only) source of sex education for many young men, it could help to explain why a large number of boys grow up with a phallocentric and impersonal approach to lovemaking.

For many men, their use of pornography is a secret, guilt-ridden affair. We probably hide it from our friends and partners in much the same way as we hid it from our parents when we were teenagers. But any man who wants to re-evaluate, and perhaps change, his relationship to pornography can take few bolder or more significant steps than being open and honest about his desire to use it. Exploring the questions suggested here with someone we trust could help us to develop a much better and emotionally healthier relationship to pornography.

## sex for sale

Tim, a 36-year-old accountant, answered an ad in a contact magazine:

I'd only been to bed with one woman before – who I'd been married to for ten years – and when we separated I wanted to get some more sexual experience. I went round to her [the prostitute's] house and we did it straight away, although I was a bit put off by the fact that she was a bit old and her baby was asleep in the next room.

That wasn't Tim's last experience with prostitutes:

> Later that year, I went to Amsterdam with the specific intention of paying for some more sex. I had sex with two prostitutes – although not at the same time – and enjoyed it. They were both young and attractive, I liked not having to worry about whether they were having a good time, although they seemed to be, and they did exactly what I asked. I'd definitely do it again, although I'd stop if I started a permanent relationship.

Paying for sex – the ultimate fantasy for some, the ultimate nightmare for others, but reality for at least 7 per cent of British men aged 16–59. That's how many have had commercial sex at least once, according to the British National Survey of Sexual Attitudes and Lifestyles. Two per cent of men have done so in the last five years, with the most likely buyers being men aged 25–34, as well as men who are widowed, separated or divorced. Professional men like Tim are also more likely to pay for sex – this could be linked to opportunities for work-related travel away from home.

Men visit prostitutes for many different reasons. It may be because of loneliness, sexual frustration or difficulties with a current partner; it could stem from a desire to try new techniques that a partner doesn't like; it could be because it offers an opportunity to have sex without emotional 'complications', closeness or any further obligation. For some men, the idea of sex with a prostitute is simply exciting in itself **105**

– it is, after all, a very common sexual fantasy – while others are turned on by the element of risk involved. If we visit prostitutes, or have a strong desire to do so, it's certainly worth thinking about why.

It may be that the answers will help us work out other, perhaps more satisfying ways in which we can get our needs met. For example, if it's because our relationship with our partner is not as we'd like it to be, it might make more sense to try sorting it out rather than visiting prostitutes. Perhaps we'd gain more from talking to our partner about why we're dissatisfied. If the idea of quick, impersonal sex appeals to us, it's possible that our use of prostitutes could reflect difficulties with intimacy or establishing long-term relationships.

One key issue for any man paying for sex is safety. Surprisingly few prostitutes are HIV positive – studies in London, Manchester and The Netherlands suggest 'only' 1–2 per cent have tested positive – although infection rates are still at least three times higher than women generally. Prostitutes who inject drugs are also much more likely to be HIV positive and all prostitutes have a higher than average risk of other sexually transmitted diseases (around 14 per cent may have a serious infection at any one time). Many men still ask prostitutes for sex without a condom, however, and are often willing to pay more for it. The vast majority of prostitutes – 98 per cent in one London study – always use condoms for vaginal sex, and any man would be well advised to do the same.

# johnny be good

For some of us, the first time we think about contraception is when we're asked to pay for an abortion. Men have traditionally seen pregnancy as a woman's affair – just 3 per cent of clients at family planning clinics are male. The reason for this is pretty obvious: men don't get pregnant. However, if we're a man who believes in equality between the sexes, taking our share of responsibility for contraception is one good way of demonstrating that we mean what we say.

Unfortunately, doctors, being mostly male, have also tended to see contraception as a woman's issue. Consequently, while there are now nine different methods of birth control for women, for men there are only two. The most popular of these is the condom; the other is a vasectomy. The so-called 'male pill', if it ever gets beyond the testing stage, is unlikely to be available until the early years of the next century. Other new male contraceptives – including a drug that causes dry ejaculations and a sperm-damaging polymer which can be inserted into tubes leading from the testes – are also still in the early stages of development.

Condoms were first used as a contraceptive and barrier to disease in Roman times. Rubber condoms emerged in the nineteenth century and the first latex condoms were introduced in the 1930s. With the advent of HIV and AIDS, the condom has returned as one of the most important forms of contraceptive, as it is the only one that provides reasonable protection against the transmission of the HIV virus. Since the mid-1980s, British condom sales have risen significantly and 107 now stand at 150 million a year. 'Johnnies' are now the main contraceptive for two-thirds of men with regular partners.

Condoms were once made out of such unerotic materials as sheep's stomachs. Today they're made out of material as little as 0.0016 inches thick; they're lubricated and anatomically shaped; they can be ribbed, flavoured, coloured and luminous; they can even play a tune when you take them out of the packet – all this and yet many men still complain that they take the fun out of making love. We've all heard the phrases – 'Using a condom is like washing your feet with your socks on', or 'You might as well eat a sweet with the wrapper on.' And despite the claims of the manufacturers, it's almost certainly true that condoms do dull sensitivity for some men. However, there may also be more deep-seated, psychological factors for many men's dislike of condoms.

For a start, condoms are a pretty wimpy, sexless affair. After all, where did you first see one? Lying in the gutter? In your parent's cupboard? A floppy piece of pink latex is hardly an icon of masculinity either; and if we're trying to show how sexually virile we are, clumsily rolling a condom over our penis is unlikely to impress – especially if we've never done it before. Many men find condoms so embarrassing and fiddly the first time that they never bother again. In some cases, men have such bad experiences with them that they find themselves unable to have an erection the next time they try to put one on.

Moreover, condoms require a break between foreplay and penetration, so if we're trying to prove what a beast we are in bed, we won't appreciate interrupting our spontaneous animal urges to fumble around in the dark. Groping around to check it hasn't slipped off or split while we're 'on the job' isn't exactly the erotic experience of the month either. Just about the only manly things you can do with condoms are to show your partner how much semen you've produced or to put one over your head and blow it up as a party trick.

Fortunately, however, we can train ourselves to get used to condoms. One good way is to masturbate with them. In the comfort of our own hand, we can learn how to get them on properly, get used to the way they feel and begin to realize that we can have a lot of fun with them. We may also want to explore all the different varieties now on the market to find the make and type that fits most comfortably. Most men who use them regularly say they no longer find them a problem, and some even say they make sex better – by delaying orgasm, sex lasts longer and the climax is therefore even more powerful.

It's not just men who don't like condoms, however – some women complain that they dull sexual sensitivity for them too. And if a woman doesn't want to use a condom, we may find ourselves struggling to convince her we should wear one, especially if we don't want to look like we're scared of pregnancy or HIV infection. Moreover, many men seem to think that if a woman is so turned-on and horny that she thinks, 'Sod the condoms', then it's OK for us to say 'Sod them' too. So if we really want to take an equal role with contraceptives, there are times when we are going to have to **109** be the one who plays the 'parent' role, puts a foot down and refuses to have sex unless it's safer.

Used properly, condoms can provide an excellent barrier against both pregnancy and HIV infection. Unfortunately, however, they're not always used as they should be. So make sure you follow the instructions on the packet and watch out particularly for the following:

- *Make sure that the condoms you buy carry a kitemark (that means their quality is tested and assured) and are also not past their sell-by date.*
- *Don't use any oil-based lubricants (Vaseline or butter, for example) when using a condom – they'll cause it to rot. Use water-based lubricants instead, such as K-Y Jelly. Other, more sensuous and human-like substances are now also available.*
- *Never reuse a condom.*
- *Make sure that the condom has not been damaged by heat.*
- *Squeeze the air out of the tip of the condom before rolling it on.*
- *Make sure, by holding the condom at its base, that the condom doesn't slip off when you remove your penis from the vagina.*
- *Condoms can be made more sensitive by placing a dab of water-based lubricant inside the tip.*

# a little snip

Despite having no children, Chris decided on a vasectomy at the age of 28:

The knot in my stomach tightened as I walked along the corridor. My heart thumped loudly. I was expecting pain. The doctor explained in detail what he was going to do and then did it. What seemed like all afternoon was in fact about seven minutes.

Back at home that evening:

I began to feel ... well, it's difficult to say, other than emotional. Close to tears and sad. For two days there was little pain, just a certain amount of discomfort. On the third day, however, my balls were really tender. I walked slowly and sprat-legged, like John Wayne after a day in the saddle. Over the next three months I had to ejaculate 10 to 20 times to get rid of any sperm left over in the tubes. I felt no lessening of my desire for sex. Physically, sex was almost exactly as it was before; if anything, the vasectomy has added to my sex life and taken nothing away. I have no regrets.

Over one in ten men with partners of child-bearing age have had a vasectomy. Most are in their 30s and 40s, although an increasing number of men in their 20s are, like Chris, now asking for 'the snip'. A vasectomy is a simple operation, rarely **111** taking more than ten minutes and performed under local anaesthetic. The vas deferens tubes, which carry the sperm from each testicle to the penis, are snipped and then tied. This involves a small cut made in the scrotum which is then sealed up with dissolvable stitches. Following the operation, there's normally some bruising and discomfort, but this usually passes after a few days. Intercourse is possible as soon as it feels comfortable, but two consecutive negative sperm tests, normally after two to four months, are required before no other contraception is necessary.

While vasectomies are considered a very safe operation – and men don't come out singing soprano – there is always the possibility of complications, such as the wound bleeding or infections. Some research has also suggested a link between vasectomies and kidney stones, prostate cancer and testicular cancer, but this remains unproven. The operation has no effect on a man's production of testosterone and a man will continue to ejaculate seminal fluid. (In fact, you won't be able to see, or feel, any difference in your semen.) However, a vasectomy is no protection against HIV infection for either the male or female.

It's pretty obvious that a vasectomy is only worth consider-ing if you are absolutely certain that you don't want any, or any more, children. In fact, any reputable clinic wouldn't perform the operation without discussing this with you first. If you have any doubts, it's probably not worth going ahead because it's very difficult (as well as expensive) to reverse a vasectomy. If you do decide that you want one, see your own doctor or a family planning clinic for further information. You should always be offered advice and counselling before the operation.

## safety first

Ever since the early 1980s, it's been known that a deadly virus can be transmitted through sexual intercourse. This disease is far more serious than syphilis or gonorrhoea and has, within little more than a decade of its discovery, infected millions of people worldwide. This disease is, of course, Acquired Immunodeficiency Syndrome, better known as AIDS.

There are several stages to the disease. First, a person becomes infected with a virus known as HIV (the Human Immunodeficiency Virus). The virus can be transmitted if the blood, semen or vaginal fluid of an infected person enters the bloodstream of another person in sufficient quantity. Fortunately, this can happen in only a few, well-known ways: through unprotected penetrative sex, through infected blood products used in medicine (although this risk has diminished since blood is now screened for HIV) and through sharing needles or syringes containing infected blood. HIV can also be transmitted from mother to child, either pre-birth, during birth or while breast-feeding.

After infection, HIV attacks the white blood cells in the body whose role is to fight off infection. In this way, over time, the immune system is weakened and the ability to fight off infections reduced. Although most people with HIV remain **113** healthy for many years, it's thought that the majority will develop an HIV-related illness within 10–12 years of infection. Such illnesses often include a malignancy (such as lymphoma or Kaposi's sarcoma) or a life-threatening opportunistic infection (such as pneumonia or tuberculosis). Somebody is diagnosed as having AIDS when they develop one or more serious infections or illnesses known to be associated with the condition. Although many people with AIDS continue to fight the disease, and may even have periods when they appear healthy and lead full lives, most eventually die. As yet, there are no cures and no sign of a vaccine, although new treatments are important in slowing down viral replication and preventing infections.

More and more people in the UK are becoming infected with HIV. Between 1984 and June 1995, there were about 24,500 known cases of HIV infection, about 21,000 of whom were men (86 per cent of the total). Many of these have gone on to contract AIDS: between 1982 and June 1995, just over 11,000 AIDS cases were reported, affecting some 10,000 men (91 per cent of the total).

So far in the UK, most cases of HIV and AIDS have affected gay men. However, the proportion of heterosexual people affected is increasing. In the year ending June 1995, 31 per cent of new HIV cases in the UK were acquired through heterosexual sex, and the World Health Organization believes that, worldwide, over 75 per cent of people with HIV acquired the infection through heterosexual intercourse. British research has also estimated that over three-quarters of those who have acquired HIV through heterosexual sex do not yet know they're HIV positive. This means that it's in all our interests to inform ourselves about HIV and AIDS and to take steps to reduce the risks of transmission.

Fortunately, an overwhelming 96 per cent of people in the UK now know that using a condom reduces the risk of getting HIV, according to Health Education Authority research. Condom use is growing, with three-quarters of adults saying that they would always use a condom with a new partner. About one-third now use condoms more often and one-quarter have reduced their number of new partners after learning about AIDS. The British National Survey of Sexual Attitudes and Lifestyles found that just 6 per cent of straight men are practising unsafe sex, defined as having two or more heterosexual partners in the last year and never using a condom.

But the risks haven't gone away – and that means safer sex is as essential for straight men as it is for gay and bisexual men. Since there's no way of telling for certain whether a partner is infected with HIV (because it takes three months before the antibodies can be detected), it makes sense to play safe. The problem for many men, especially straight men, is that practising safer sex not only means using condoms – not always the most popular sexual activity – but also involves actually talking to, and perhaps negotiating with, a partner about sex. As we've already established, that's something many of us find very difficult – it can certainly feel easier to just get our willy out, wave it around a bit, stick it in and hope for the best. We 115 may also think that admitting we're worried about HIV sends a message to a female partner that we must be bisexual – or just plain scared. There's no easy way out of these concerns, except to say that if we take steps to improve our communication skills in every aspect of our life, discussing our sex life will become easier too. When it comes to HIV, there's certainly every incentive to try, since however scary it feels to admit our worries, it's definitely less frightening than being told we're HIV positive.

If you want to have safer sex, remember:

- *Unprotected penetrative sex, whether vaginal or anal, is the major route of HIV transmission. Unprotected anal intercourse – whether between two men or a man and a woman – is the highest risk activity.*
- *Unprotected vaginal intercourse with an infected woman is particularly risky during the woman's period.*
- *HIV is more easily transmitted if either partner has another sexually transmitted disease.*
- *The best protection against HIV transmission through intercourse is to use a condom – properly.*
- *Oral sex has a very much lower risk of HIV transmission than anal or vaginal intercourse, but transmission is theoretically possible when semen, vaginal fluid or menstrual blood come into contact with the mouth, particularly if there are bleeding gums, ulcers or infections in the mouth.*
- *The risks of oral sex can be reduced by not getting semen*

or menstrual blood in the mouth (by stopping before ejaculation or not having oral sex during a woman's period). To be really safe, use a condom or a dental dam (a square piece of latex placed over the vagina). Flavoured varieties of both are available.

• There's no evidence of transmission of HIV through kissing, licking, body rubbing or mutual masturbation. These forms of sex are therefore the safest. Sex toys such as dildos and vibrators, however, should not be shared.

It's also worth thinking about having an HIV test. On one level, all that's involved is a small blood sample taken from the arm which takes a few hours to analyse. (Some clinics will give the result later the same day; others may ask clients to wait up to a week.) However, it's also a procedure that may well be frightening – whatever the result – and, anyone told that they have the virus may well experience deep feelings of shock, anger, fear or grief. Having a test certainly isn't something to be rushed into – indeed, most people discuss it first with their partner and friends and then have pre-test counselling at a clinic.

A test may be a good idea for anyone very worried about having been infected – perhaps because they've discovered a partner has injected drugs – or if they're now in a stable, monogamous relationship and the result will help them and their partner decide what it's safe to do when making love. (The partner may need to have a test too.) If they should test **117** positive, early detection can enable them to take action to stay healthy: they could be prescribed antiviral drugs to help delay the onset of symptoms or reduce their severity, and they could also boost their immune system through diet and exercise. If the immune system does become seriously compromised, antibiotics can be given to cut the risk of developing pneumonia. These advantages, however, have to be weighed against other consequences of a positive result, including the reactions of whoever they choose to tell as well as their own feelings.

Sex poses no problems for the real man. There's been no looking back for him since he lost his virginity well before puberty. Ever since then, he's been a virtual sex machine, bedding women at will and giving each and every one the orgasm of a lifetime. For most of us, however, sex simply isn't like that. It can be fun, of course, but there's also plenty to worry about. We may well be having problems with coming too soon, or with getting it up, and we might believe another couple of inches on the end of our wedding tackle wouldn't go amiss. But if we can acknowledge our worries and vulnerabilities about sex and start to talk about them with our partner or friends – or perhaps even a therapist – we can begin to improve our sexual self-esteem and to enjoy sex even more. Realizing that almost all men share similar anxieties can be a particularly big help – it's both reassuring and provides the basis for men to share their experiences and **118** support each other. The complete man understands that really good sex is primarily about learning to become more intimate, sensuous and relaxed and that his status as a man doesn't depend on his performance in the sack.

chapter five

# violence:
# the peaceful man

## rambo's roots

For most of us, violence is something we happily leave behind in the school playground. We've had enough dead legs to know that fighting doesn't pay, and while Chinese burns may be one way of getting our rubber back from a classmate, we've probably realized it's not an appropriate negotiating technique for the boardroom. Nevertheless, there are still many men who continue to punch, kick and fight their way through adult life, whether it's the odd ruck on the football terraces or the systematic beating of partners or children.

So what is it that encourages some men to continue to use physical force? In many cases, it's simply the fact that violence begets violence. If we come from a background in which hitting people was an everyday occurrence, we may well continue to see it as a legitimate way of getting our needs met. Men who were frequently hit as boys often pass this on to others as part of a cycle of violence – when they feel hurt, they want to hurt back. But that's only part of the story, because

violence is a predominantly male phenomenon. Over 90 per

cent of offenders found guilty of 'crimes against the person' are male. Virtually all rapists are men, and men constitute the overwhelming majority of military personnel in Britain (the only group in society trained and encouraged to act violently). So to really understand why men are violent, we need to look at what's influenced us as we've grown up.

Inflicting violence on others can certainly make a man feel manly. After all, Rambo's not a real man because of his dress sense. Like so many tough guys, he comes close to the pinnacle of real man-ness because of the immense power he wields through his physical might. It does indeed seem as if violence is one of the most effective ways of asserting control. Mr Jones can sleep with our wife, supervise us at work, even beat us at Mortal Kombat, but if we've got his head in a real (rather than a virtual) arm-lock, then we're the one on top.

So overpowering someone through violence can make us feel good about ourselves – it's what the inner Arnie's all about. Can you remember the last time you beat someone up (if you ever have)? Even if it was at school, you can probably recall some of the feelings that went with victory. Guilt and shame, perhaps, for doing something 'naughty', but also an overwhelming feeling of pride. A sense that you'd stood up like a man, proved your self-worth and exerted your superiority over another male. And if we feel good about beating someone else up, we could be tempted to try to recreate that feeling again and again.

Most men don't, of course, but those who feel particularly insecure about their masculinity may be more inclined to turn **121** to violence as a way of boosting their sense of self-esteem. If we feel we're a failure at work, if we're skint, if others are pushing us around, violence may seem a means of gaining some dignity and respect. For men who feel powerless or that their authority is being challenged, violence might seem like the only possible way of getting what they want. When words fail – and they can all too easily fail for men – aggression may seem the most appropriate alternative.

Winning a fight may make us feel better, but can you remember the last time you lost one? When the school bully knelt on your shoulders and spat in your face? Or when you were mugged walking down the street? Experiences of defeat can frequently leave lasting scars, although usually more of the psychological than physiological variety. To be physically over-powered by another person in such a direct way is seriously humiliating, a definite negation of our manhood. All our control is gone. As the phlegm fell from the bully's mouth, we were powerless to stop it. We were at his mercy.

Because it's so painful to be defeated, even walking away from fights can lead to feelings of shame. If someone in a bar behaves threateningly, it can bring up two very contradictory feelings. On the one hand, we might want to avoid getting hurt in a pointless fight, but on the other hand, we might not want to feel the embarrassment of being pushed around by some drunken yob. Not surprisingly, then, some men take what at the time seems the least painful option – they respond with violence when provoked. They may end up in the local hospital, but at least their masculinity is still intact. Such an attitude of honour before death may seem noble, but it's also responsible for the injury, or much worse, of millions of men – from the boxing ring to the battlefield.

The feelings violence arouses are often intensified when conflict occurs in the presence of others. Being beaten up might feel bad, but if it's in front of someone else – particularly a woman – it can leave us feeling completely humiliated and disempowered. As men, we've probably come to the conclusion that we won't be loved if we can't stand up for ourselves. Being roughed up in the school playground usually earned us the contempt of the class. And from countless Hollywood movies, we've learnt that beautiful women always go for the toughest guys. The man who's beaten to the floor may have his forehead wiped by the movie's sex bomb, but it's soon evident that she doesn't really respect him any more.

In fact, the entertainment industry has probably had a major influence on male attitudes. When we watch Bruce Lee kung fu-ing his way through Shanghai, we may not try to copy his behaviour down our local high street, but it does give us a sense that violence is something exciting, manly and acceptable. To be fair, few Hollywood heroes are actually advocates of random, senseless violence. But what they do suggest is that violence is about the only reliable means of defending ourselves, our loved ones, our community and our honour. The image of man as protector is pervasive on both the silver screen and television – from *Batman* to *Death Wish* to *The A-Team*. When things get tough for Bruce Willis in his *Die Hard* movies, you won't find him in a group therapy session **123** with the baddies. He's far too busy climbing lift shafts, defusing bombs and running barefoot across acres of broken glass.

When young boys play games like Cowboys and Indians, it can reinforce the idea that fighting is exciting and acceptable. Warfare and death are turned into dramatic interludes which make the rest of life look dull. The latest generation of computerized games continue to perpetuate the idea that the best fun you can have is to kill people. And, as we get older, news reporting of war takes the place of Space Invader machines – we can sit back and enjoy watching rockets darting through the Iraqi night sky and down Saddam Hussein's bunker. When war is so technical and distant, we might be forgiven for forgetting that over 60 million men in military service (and over 140 million people in all) are believed to have died in warfare over the last 500 years (according to the Lentz Peace Research Laboratory).

In fact, the idea that war – in reality, state-sanctioned violence – is a valid option for resolving international disputes is often reinforced by governments and the media. When Argentina invaded the Falkland Islands in 1982 and Iraq invaded Kuwait in 1990, there seemed no serious alternative to force. This has the effect of legitimizing the role of violence in society generally. After all, if governments believe that when you can't get what you want by talking, you can then justifiably lash out with everything you've got, they can't easily expect their citizens not to apply the same principles to their own lives.

124     Finally, men can often mete out – or, at least, accept

– violence because of the way in which our feelings have been repressed, in particular our ability to empathize with others. All this distances us from others and makes it harder to see them as people just like us. In fact, in our minds, we often turn them into objects, making it easier for us to treat them badly. It's not surprising that, in war, soldiers are encouraged to objectify the enemy – calling them 'the Hun', 'Gooks' or 'Argies' – so as to make them seem less human and therefore easier to kill.

## running scared

Despite all this, most of us are not advocates of violence. At the same time, however, the threat of violence can still have a direct impact on us. Suppose, for instance, you're driving down the road when the driver in front brakes, gets out of their car and starts walking towards you with a menacing look. What would you do if (a) they were a 65-year-old man, (b) a middle-aged woman, or (c) a 6-foot skinhead? The chances are you'd be a lot more likely to hit the accelerator with the skinhead closing in on you. The capacity for someone to inflict violence on us – along with shame and humiliation – can have a big influence on the way we respond to them. Although we may not be aware of it, often the first thing we do when we meet another man is to size up his physical strength, and if we feel that he could overpower us, we may treat him with a lot more respect and caution. Just remember the reverence with which the school bully was treated.

Of course, the way we respond to other men's capacity for **125** violence will very much depend on our own. If we're used to fighting and feel very confident about our physical strength, we're not likely to see other men as so much of a threat. On the other hand, if we've never won a fight and feel as if virtually all men could beat us to a pulp – as many of us do – then it's likely to leave a sense of insecurity and fear around other men. We may feel scared to get into serious arguments or to say 'no' to men who are a lot bigger than us. It can make us feel nervous when sitting in rough bars or when we walk down dark roads late at night. What can make these feelings worse is that it's often difficult for men to talk about their fear of violence with others; so we don't realize that many other men probably feel just as we do.

It could be worth reflecting on how our relationships with other men might be different if we didn't see them as potential adversaries. If we weren't constantly sizing them up, checking out who might be about to explode, who could beat us and who we might stand a better chance against, then not only might we feel a lot more relaxed, but we also might be more open to developing a wider range of friendships. We'd look a lot less threatening ourselves too – we often keep our face and body tight and drawn to hide our fear as well as to deter – making it more likely that other men (and women) would be interested in getting to know us.

Although we may feel scared of other men, it can be a very different matter entirely when it comes to women. Few of us feel physically threatened by women, and though we may not want to admit it, this can have an important effect on the way we relate to them. We may feel less obliged to take what they say seriously, or to do the things they ask, because we believe they're less able to enforce their demands through violence. If every woman had muscles the size of the Incredible Hulk's, or a Kalashnikov under her arm, imagine how differently we might behave.

# bringing it home

For Geoffrey, a 35-year-old marketing manager, it first started during an argument about a problem they were having with some builders:

> Jane was having a go at me because I'd not done something I said I would. I got so angry, I grabbed her by the arms and shook her hard enough to cause some bruises. I didn't know what else to do; I'd run out of ideas and lost the vocabulary to end the argument in any other way.

This wasn't the last time Geoffrey was violent to Jane:

> I'd been having problems at work which were affecting my self-confidence and ability to cope. I tried to shrug it off but, deep-down, I felt deflated and worthless. I felt I'd been unfairly criticized at work and the last person I wanted to be criticized by was Jane. That's when the violence would happen. It could be completely innocuous

**127**

things that would trigger it. She would say something like 'Why haven't you done this?' or 'Why can't you remember where anything is?' and I would start seething. I thought it was so unfair. I just wanted her to shut up. I normally shook her, although I also pushed her on to the bed. Once I slapped her very hard across the face.

Geoffrey's behaviour might sound extreme, but imagine yourself coming home from a tough day at the office to discover that your flat is still a tip – your partner promised she'd clean it up, but instead she's lying in bed watching *Neighbours*. You ask her if she's made any supper and discover that she's about to go out for the evening with an old flame. What would you do in such a situation? Forget about things and make your own supper? Wander off in a sulk? Tell her how angry and irritated you are? Or would you feel like hitting her? Do you actually go the whole hog and start to push, slap, punch, kick or even attack her with objects?

The violent option is not as rare as you might think. According to The North London Domestic Violence Survey of almost 600 women, almost one-third said that they'd suffered violence from their partner – and that excludes rape and 'less severe' violence such as grabbing, pushing or shaking. The same survey asked over 400 men about their behaviour. One-fifth said that they'd hit their partner and one half believed that they might if, for example, she was unfaithful or arrived home late at night without prior warning. A government

review of a large number of studies concluded that 'domestic violence constitutes a pervasive problem' and that women are on the receiving end in the overwhelming majority of cases. Domestic violence is also known to occur in some gay relationships.

Assaults tend to happen when a man feels angry or frustrated. It may be, for instance, that his partner's spent money on things he doesn't approve of; or else he may feel that she's putting him down and undermining his self-confidence. Often, however, the man's frustration will have little to do with his partner. A late train, a losing streak on the horses, a dressing down from his boss – almost any negative experience could leave him in such a state of frustration or anger that his partner's cold supper becomes the final trigger for a violent outburst.

When men assault their partners, they often feel like they've 'blown a gasket' and 'lost control'; that it's an involuntary, spontaneous act. However, the fact that many perpetrators of domestic violence don't lash out at men in the same way suggests that they see women as easier targets. For a start, their partner is less likely to hit back and, if she does, it's unlikely to hurt as much as being thumped by another man. With so much indifference to the problem of domestic violence by the police and judiciary (although this is slowly changing), men may also feel that they can get away with hitting their partner without any serious fear of legal retribution.

What's more, if domestic violence was simply a product of frustration, we'd all be doing it. The fact that most of us don't hit our partner when we get angry suggests that men who do **129** often have an underlying belief that violence against women is legitimate. It may be, for instance, that their father attacked their mother and, consequently, they see domestic violence as an almost normal part of family life. It may also be that they hold very traditional views of the gender roles and feel that it's justifiable for a man to assert his authority in a relationship, through violence if necessary.

Domestic violence is often used by men as a 'control mechanism'. Through assaulting their partners – or just by the threat of it – they can ensure that she does what they want. So the dinner's ready on time, the flat's clean and she never goes out with anyone she's not 'supposed' to. Men may also turn to violence when they feel incapable of asking for what they want in any other way. In fact, many men actually feel quite powerless in the relationship and violence is a desperate, last-ditch attempt by them to try to exert some measure of control.

Although men may feel their violence is justified at the time, many perpetrators of domestic violence feel guilty or remorseful after their attack. They may realize that what they've done is wrong, or else be scared that their partners will now leave them. Flowers, chocolates, apologies and assurances of no more violence often follow. In some cases, this can persuade the woman that the violence will not recur; in others, the partner will have little alternative but to stay in the home as children or lack of money prevent her from leaving. Men may also deny the extent of their violence after the event – both to themselves, their partners and others – in an attempt to

**130** minimize their feelings of guilt and to deny responsibility for what happened. Domestic violence seldom occurs just once in a relationship – unless the woman leaves straight away. (This rarely happens; in fact, it's thought that women are assaulted an average of 35 times before they do leave.)

Obviously enough, domestic violence can be extremely damaging. As well as suffering severe physical injuries and possibly even death, victims of domestic violence can feel humiliated, frightened, degraded, powerless, self-blaming, trapped, intimidated and depressed. Perpetrators of domestic violence, too, rarely achieve much in the long run. Sooner or later they're likely to lose their partner, along with any children they may have had together. What's more, the courts are at last beginning to hand out increasingly severe sentences to men who assault their wives or lovers.

A number of programmes have been set up to help men deal with the problems of domestic violence. Normally men can refer themselves, though in some cases they can only participate through a court order. A man joining a programme will probably begin with several sessions of one-to-one coun-selling, in which he'll be pushed to acknowledge the full extent of his violence rather than keeping it a silent secret. He may also be encouraged to explore the roots of his violence, whether feelings of inadequacy, sexist attitudes or an abusive past. After the one-to-one sessions, he may join a weekly group where he'll be taught anger-management techniques. The group may also have a peer regulatory function – men report back on their behaviour during the week and are challenged by the other men if they have assaulted their **131** partners. Programmes normally run for about six months.

Organizers of programmes for violent men claim that they are successful for most men who complete them. However, it's also argued that such courses are a soft option, can leave violent men in the home to continue attacking their partners, and that it would be better to have a stronger response by the criminal justice system. It's also been said that programmes for violent men divert much-needed funding from women's refuges. Despite their drawbacks, however, these programmes do seem to offer some hope of a solution to this deep-seated problem.

Clive, a 39-year-old solicitor, certainly believes a programme has helped him. After his wife Deborah left him because of his violence, he realized that he had to sort himself out. It was difficult at first to admit that what he'd done was wrong, but he found that once he was able to do that the floodgates then opened. He started off with a few one-to-one sessions, which he feels were very important because they helped him to learn to be more open. After that he joined a small support group:

One very important part of the process for me was the 'personal contract', which I wrote down in the early stages. It contained my objectives and I had to keep referring back to these. Throughout the programme, I also kept an 'anger diary' in which I had to be honest and fair with myself about my feelings and behaviour. Part of the therapy was coming to terms with what I'd done and admitting all the details rather than minimizing it. I did find it painful to talk about the past and I wanted to draw a veil over it, but I knew it was important to remember what I did. I've learned to stop the anger or to walk away if I feel it. I've questioned a lot of the attitudes and motives which were in-built. I've realized that women aren't sex objects, there to do what I want. I see women more as people. I also feel that I'm a much better person now.

# on the other foot

Recently, there's been increasing media coverage of domestic violence incidents by women against men – the so-called 'battered husband' phenomenon. Some research has suggested that it's just as common as male violence against women – one American study found that wives committed an average of 10.3 acts of violence against their husbands each year, while husbands averaged 8.8 acts against their wives. This research is atypical, however, and not widely accepted.

There may still be some men who are genuine victims of domestic violence. These men can face particular problems: first, of being believed by anyone; and secondly, of feeling pretty ashamed and embarrassed about their dilemma. Contacting the police may therefore seem out of the question and there are very few agencies which can help, although victim support services may be able to offer some assistance.

While few of us are regular victims of female violence, there may well have been times when we've been hit by a woman in 133 the midst of an argument. When this happens, we can feel tempted to hit her back. However, without wanting to suggest that we should simply let her continue being violent, there are a couple of issues to think about before retaliating. In general, men can hit harder than women, so a punch thrown in anger may be a lot harder than we think. And, what's more, a woman's punches may be able to hurt us, but it's very unlikely that she's going to be able to use her physical force to coerce us into doing something we don't want to do.

## a clip round the ear

How would you feel, wandering through your local supermarket, if you saw one person whacking another person around the head, screaming abuse at them and threatening further violence if they didn't shut up? You'd probably think the attacker was a headcase; you might tell the shop manager and, if you were feeling brave, you might even intervene. So why is it that when the person being hit is a child, many of us hardly take our eyes from the supermarket shelves and carry on filling our trolley regardless? Hitting children just seems to be the norm. In one American survey, 86 per cent of respondents thought that young people needed strong, physical discipline; 70 per cent thought it normal, necessary and good to slap a 12-year-old.

Violence towards children may have many of the same roots as violence towards women. We see it as acceptable, we don't really respect the victims' rights, and we're not afraid of them hitting us back. Many adults also see violence against children as an effective means of teaching them the difference between right and wrong. There's no evidence that this works, however. If our dad smacked us for trying to strangle the cat, it may well have stopped us – but only when he was around.

Besides being physically dangerous, if we hit children it can leave them with lasting psychological scars. They can feel bitter towards us as well as the world in general, or feel afraid of other men. Given the fact that boys tend to be struck more often and harder than girls, this may partly explain why men are more violent than women. Being hit as a child can teach us that it's legitimate for big people to hit little people, so perpetuating the cycle of violence into another generation. A report by The Commission on Children and Violence, published in 1995, argued that 'non-violence should be consistently preferred and promoted' and 'all discipline should be positive and children should be taught pro-social values and behaviour including non-violent conflict resolution.'

## unilateral disarmament

Dealing with our violence against other men, women or children isn't easy. Even if professional help is sought, it still requires great commitment to break through old patterns of behaviour. However, if we are determined to end our violence, there are several positive steps we can take for ourselves.

- **Keep an 'anger diary':** *every day, write down details of any situation in which you felt angry or felt you could become angry. Describe what sparked off your anger and assess how strong the feeling was on a scale of 1–100. Write down what you did – for example, you may have hit someone or smashed something. Finally, note down any thoughts about how you could have handled the situation without violence. The idea behind the diary is that you'll be able to better understand the causes of your anger and the kind of situations in which you become angry. You'll also be able to identify alternative courses of action and monitor your progress.*

- **Take 'time outs':** *this involves deciding to take a fixed period of time (usually 60 minutes) away from your partner or child when you recognize that you're becoming angry. Tell them about your decision beforehand and, when a situation arises, tell them that you are going to take a time out. Then leave the house – perhaps go for a walk – and return at the agreed time. When you return, try to work out the problem calmly. If you get angry again, agree to leave it to one side until another time.*

- **Follow the '6-feet rule':** *in a situation where you feel you're going to become violent, make the decision not to go nearer than 6 feet from the other person. At this distance, you can't hit them.*

- **Avoid situations in which you know you're likely to get angry or violent:** *this may mean cutting down on your* *drinking or maybe not going to football matches on a Saturday afternoon.*

- **Avoid depersonalizing:** *notice how you think about people when you get angry with them. You may, for example, think of your partner as 'a bitch' or your child as 'a little sod'. When you're angry, it could help if you continue to call them by their real name – the more human they seem, the less likely you are to be violent.*

- **Be assertive:** *learn to ask for what you want directly rather than having to demand it through violence. Talk as openly as you can about how you feel. At the same time, be ready to listen to the needs and feelings of others. Be prepared to negotiate – you may well be able to get some, perhaps even most, of your needs met without violence.*

## sexual abuse

When we think of the word 'rape' it often conjures up images of a sex-starved stranger in a dirty raincoat attacking a defenceless woman in a dark alley. The reality, however, is usually very different. For a start, most rapists are known to their victims and may even be their fathers, brothers, husbands or 'friends'. A Granada television *World in Action* programme in 1991 surveyed over 1,000 women and, disturbingly, found that one in four had been raped, one in seven by their husbands.

Although rape has many complex causes, it's rarely caused **137** by male sexual frustration. Men who rape often have long-term partners who they regularly sleep with. Besides which, a man who was simply desperate for sex could go to a prostitute. Rapists generally use sexual assault as a way of dealing with their anger with women: they want to humiliate or degrade them or to 'teach them a lesson'. They may have a deep-seated hatred or fear of women, or see women as the root of their problems and so use rape as a form of revenge. Rape is rarely a spontaneous act; it's usually well planned and thought out. Rapists often succeed in humiliating their victims: they can be severely traumatized – as well as physically injured – and left with long-term psychological problems. It's also been said that, even though not all men rape, rape benefits all men by keeping women in a state of fear.

'Date rape' or rape in marriage can occur when men don't take women's refusals of sex seriously. They may believe that if she says 'no' she really means 'yes', and that once a woman has shown any degree of sexual interest men have the right to do what they want. Rapists may also believe myths such as 'Women who wear short skirts are asking for it', or 'Women secretly enjoy having sex forced on them.' In other words, some rapists may see their behaviour as a perfectly normal part of their sexuality and not necessarily abusive at all.

For example, a man who goes out on a date with a woman and pays the bill may expect sex in return. If it's denied, he may become aggressive, verbally or physically. Sometimes he'll succeed in scaring the woman sufficiently to force her to have

sex without actual violence having taken place. He may then

interpret her behaviour as freely given consent. Sometimes, he may wrestle the woman to the ground; if she stops struggling out of fear or because she feels she's less likely to be hurt than if she resists, then again, the man may assume she's consenting.

In the last ten years, it's also become clear that the sexual abuse of children is a major social problem. One study of over 1,200 16–21-year-olds by North London University found that 59 per cent of the women, and 27 per cent of the men, had been sexually abused at least once before they were 18. (If 'less serious' forms of abuse – such as 'flashing' – are excluded, the prevalence figures are one in five for women and one in fourteen for men.) Abusers are often men who were themselves abused as boys. When a boy is abused his sense of his own masculinity is undermined and this can lead to the development of an insecure male identity which lacks the confidence to develop normal sexual relationships. Men may also see children as willing sexual partners with adult sexual preferences. Sometimes abusers convince themselves that they are actually doing the child a favour by introducing them to sex in what they falsely believe is a caring way.

Until recently, men convicted of sexual abuse offences were usually just locked up without any attempt being made to alter their thoughts and behaviour. However, the government has introduced a treatment programme for prisoners and a few similar projects are available in the community for convicted offenders, the best known of which was the pioneering Gracewell Clinic in Birmingham. Until it closed in 1993, the 139

Gracewell programme focused on getting men to admit the extent of their sexual abuse, develop an ability to empathize with the victims of their abuse, and change their fantasies. Gracewell claimed that, since it opened in 1988, none of its clients had been convicted of a further offence.

Men who have not yet actually abused but who are concerned about the possibility – perhaps because they regularly have rape fantasies, find themselves becoming sexually aroused by children, or seek out 'hard-core' pornography depicting sexual abuse – should consider contacting a counsellor or therapist. Discussing the desire to abuse may well not only prevent it from happening but also help to improve their self-esteem and the quality of their relationships with others.

While only a minority of us will ever use physical force or threats to compel a woman to have sex with us, the issues brought up by rape are still relevant to us all. To what extent, for instance, are we prepared to coerce a woman into making love? Would we just 'touch her up' to try to get her turned on or would we go further through the use of guilt, emotional blackmail or intimidation? The line between encouragement and force is often a thin one. Moreover, we have to ask ourselves whether part of us believes in the myths about women and rape. If so, is it possible that these assumptions affect the way we behave sexually with women? And how would we respond to a woman, perhaps a partner, who had been raped? Would part of us hold her responsible? Would we believe that she wouldn't have gone to that part of town, worn that dress or

accepted that lift if she hadn't really been 'asking for it'?

# sexual abuse of men

Most of us imagine that rape only happens to women. However, men do get raped too, and not just in prisons. It could happen to any of us, no matter how masculine or heterosexual we may believe we are. In the United States, for example, where many states have rape laws which apply to both men and women, 5–10 per cent of reported rape victims are male. While it's often imagined that most perpetrators of male rape are gay men, in fact most are straight and, in many cases, it's the victims who are gay. Male rape is perpetrated for much the same reasons as female rape: it's a way of expressing power and control over the victim; it usually has little to do with sex.

Men who are raped can experience psychological traumas as severe as those affecting women. Being raped can undermine a man's sense of his masculinity – after all, men are supposed to be able to defend themselves and penetrate others rather than be penetrated. Rape can also lead straight men to question their heterosexuality. They may believe that they somehow invited the attack or that they secretly enjoyed it. (When a man is raped, the stimulation of his prostate may give him an erection and possibly even lead to ejaculation.) Male victims of rape may also feel reluctant to go to the police for fear of humiliation, even though some police forces are now beginning to set up special services.

The psychological effects of abuse on boys can be just as devastating as the rape of adult men, if not more so. Adult 'survivors' may experience deep feelings of shame or guilt, **141** a need to be constantly in control, a fear of intimacy, compulsive sexual behaviour, feelings of asexuality, isolation, and an inability to say 'no'. Sometimes, they can feel very detached from the world so that nothing actually feels real. In some cases, the experience of being abused is linked to the abuse of others. Fortunately, men (and women) who have been abused, either as children or adults, can now get support from an increasing number of organizations. These can provide telephone and one-to-one counselling and they organize support groups for men who have been sexually abused. Part of the philosophy of these organizations is that men should try not to see themselves as helpless victims but as people with the resources to cope and recover from their abuse.

Harvey, a 42-year-old teacher, is one man who has survived a long history of sexual abuse:

I was first abused when I was seven by a friend of the family. I felt I was getting no love and affection at home and he would let me sit on his knee, buy me sweets and give me pocket money. One evening, outside the back door, he put his hand down my trousers and started touching me. I didn't know what was going on but I didn't want it to stop because I needed his affection.

Harvey's father died when he was 11 and his mother married the man who had abused him:

By this time I was having oral sex. He coerced me with excuses like 'I just love you and if you loved me you'd do this for me.' Then he started buggering me, usually on a Sunday morning when my mother was downstairs cooking lunch. This continued until I was 15.

The abuse had a devastating effect:

I felt different, dirty and had a constant feeling of shame. I felt confused about my sexuality. I started behaving self-destructively, ending up in a Spanish prison for smuggling cocaine. My marriage broke up because I found sex difficult to deal with – I used to cut out emotionally and I felt like an abuser in bed. I went on to use a lot of drugs and had constant suicidal fantasies. I didn't begin to recover until I contacted a survivor's organization and started counselling. I developed new ways of looking after myself and I'm at last learning to feel comfortable about my sexuality.

## the noble warrior

While most of us recoil from the idea of cruel, random or purposeless violence, we probably still believe that violence can be legitimate. We may think violence is justified in self-defence – when an individual or a country is attacked – or perhaps to put right a greater wrong, such as for one country to depose a brutal dictator in another. We may well warm to **143** the ideal of the 'noble warrior', the just man who fights only when provoked, who never glories in death and who grieves for those he kills.

The problem with any justification of violence, however plausible, is that it's always open to wide interpretation. It's not difficult for anybody to find an apparently good excuse to act aggressively. But there's no need to get drawn into a discussion of the acceptability or morality of violence to realize that there's one powerful alternative – non-violent resistance. The Indian independence leader, Mahatma Gandhi, was one of the foremost exponents of this type of action. Whatever the provocation from the British rulers of India, Gandhi's followers would never raise their fists, let alone take up arms. In one famous incident in 1930, 2,500 Indians marched in protest to a government salt works, 150 miles north of Bombay. As they approached the site, the police attacked with clubs. The marchers offered no resistance besides continuing to move forwards. The salt works were defended, over 300 protesters were injured, and two were killed, but the action inspired many others to support Indian independence and severely damaged the credibility of the British Government around the world.

As Gandhi demonstrated, non-violent resistance is not the same as cowardice. It's not about giving up and running away. Rather, it's about standing your ground and staring your opponent in the eye. It's about attempting to reach the adult human being in him rather than the frustrated and enraged 'little boy' who is temporarily in control. It's about trying to communicate rather than fight. In fact, it's very much a positive assertion of needs and rights. It requires great courage and determination and, of course, carries with it the risk of physical injury. But such action can work – ultimately, Gandhi was successful; India became an independent nation.

Of course, if you're attacked by a 15-stone Nazi and his Rottweiler, you don't have to pretend you're Gandhi. You could try to persuade him not to hit you but no-one would blame you if you decided to run away or, if you knew how, flatten him with a well-aimed karate chop. The point is that there are a range of options, there's not just the violent one. The real man allows himself only a limited choice (we all know what the inner Arnie wants us to do – convert the Nazi into 'dead meat') – but the complete man knows he has several alternatives.

We all know what the real man's like when it comes to violence: he's tough, fearless and decisive as well as fair, just and merciful. Of course, in reality, most violent men fall far short of the ideal of the 'noble warrior'. Their violence is essentially a means of being in control – who you can beat up you can dominate, whether it's another country, another man, a woman, a child or even a dog. But while not all men perpetrate violence, almost all men are affected by it. It influences how we hold our bodies, how we perceive other men, how we talk to them and how we measure our own self-worth. We all live with the knowledge (and, for many of us, the fear) that at some point we'll have to fight to prove 145 ourselves. Men who are violent can take steps to change, however – there are now effective anger-management techniques any man can learn. Instead of trying to get what we want through aggression, we can take steps to become more assertive – in other words, to ask and negotiate rather than just take. This requires improving our communication and relationship skills. The complete man realizes that his value as a human being is not determined by the size of his fists or his ability to injure or kill. He knows that a growing sense of personal empowerment will enable him to become a truly assertive yet also peaceful man.

# bodies:
# the healthy man

## body beautiful

It's a hot summer Sunday. You've been working like a lunatic all week and today you've decided you're going to take a well-deserved break – down to the seaside for a spot of sunbathing. It sounds like a great idea but, when you finally arrive on the beach and start unbuttoning your shirt, you're not so sure. Do you really want to parade your pale chest and beer gut in front of the other beach-goers? Seeing a couple of attractive young women nearby heightens your anxiety. And when you notice a group of bronzed, muscular volleyball players you can't take it any more. Ashamed of your puny stature, you scuttle off into the darkness of the amusement arcades. It may be noisy, aggressive and expensive, but at least no-one's going to see your flab.

If that's a story you can relate to, then you're not alone. Since the days when Charles Atlas's 7-stone weakling got sand kicked in his face, those of us who don't have a build like a bronzed Adonis can feel ashamed and embarrassed about the way we look. Real men have a stomach as defined as a washboard, biceps the size of melons, and pectorals like armour plating. And if we fall far short of this masculine ideal, we may feel less than attractive – despite the fact that a *New Woman* magazine survey found that only 7 per cent of women considered it 'very important' that their partner had a good body and only 18 per cent were put off by a paunch. With the growing numbers of beautiful men's bodies to compare ourselves to – from the Chippendales to men featured in women's pornography to men in aftershave adverts – there's probably never been a time when men have felt under more pressure to retrieve the Bullworker from the back of the closet.

The 'ideal' male body is hard. It's robust, it's angular, it's invulnerable. It's more like a Challenger tank than something made from human flesh. Unlike the 'perfect' female body, there are no rounded bits or curves, no softness or gentleness. The desired male body projects toughness and power; it inspires both envy and fear; it generates self-confidence and self-assuredness. Many men believe a muscular physique will not only make them look stronger, powerful and more manly, but that it's also more attractive and desirable. For them, muscles offer far more than a way of ensuring that sand will never get kicked in their direction. That's why an estimated 500,000 British men are now regularly working out and why bodybuilding is one of the fastest growing sports.

But there's something about the taut Gladiator look that's also designed to keep our emotions in check. When we're holding our stomach in, our biceps firm and our legs tense, **148** there's little opportunity to express very much in the way of feelings. To be emotional, we need a body that's relaxed and free, that isn't afraid of letting go, that can shake when we cry, jump around when we're excited, and scream with delight when we're happy.

## where's the body?

Stop! Before you read any more of this book, ask yourself a question. How is your body feeling right now? Take a few minutes to take some deep breaths, relax and think about it.

What did you discover? That you've once more found the seat on the train with the springs sticking up your backside? That your stomach's feeling queasy from last night's Häagen-Dazs and chocolate fudge-cake surprise? That your partner's half-hearted attempt at a massage has left your shoulders feeling more battle-axed than relaxed? The chances are you discovered a few sensations you hadn't previously been aware of. But you've also probably realized just how hard it is to get in touch with your body. There could be many reasons for this – a hangover, exhaustion, not understanding the question – but a big one is that, as men, we're too often detached from our physical being. We may know what we look like on the outside, but on the inside we often can't feel a thing. Much of the time our body can almost seem as if it's numb, and physical sensations like pain, discomfort or even pleasure frequently go by virtually unnoticed.

The problem is that we often seem to cut off from the neck downwards. We see our body and mind as separate rather **149** than integrated, with our 'self' residing in our head and our body as something almost alien. We're a bit like a Dalek and its mechanical exoskeleton – we need our body to keep us alive, mobile and hopefully attractive, but the feelings and sensations going on outside our brains are not credited with too much importance. You can see an extreme version of this in the popular image of the hero who battles on regardless of his wounds.

So where does this mind/body split come from? In part it can be traced back to the foundations of Christianity and the notion of the sinfulness of the flesh and the holiness of the spirit. Descartes, the seventeenth-century philosopher, further developed the idea that the physical and mental realms are separate. After all, he didn't postulate, 'I feel queasy after a Häagen-Dazs and chocolate fudge-cake surprise therefore I am'! His famous axiom, 'I think therefore I am', is perhaps the clearest statement of a philosophy that distinguishes mind from body and puts the mental first. As men, we also have few biological mechanisms to remind us of our body's day-to-day existence. We all know that shaving every day is far worse than a woman's monthly period, pregnancy, childbirth and the menopause combined, but at the same time, a woman's biological clock regularly brings her attention back to her body.

Detachment from our body is also related to the issue of control. Suppose you wake up in the morning with an aching back. Are you going to let it stop you from going to work? Your **150** inner Arnie certainly won't. No self-respecting Terminator would take a day off just because his parts had got a bit rusty! To exert control over our lives, we have to put mind over matter and cut ourselves off from our bodies. Any feelings or sensations become an obstacle to be overcome rather than an ally to be listened to. We just can't afford to let our body get in the way of our conscious will. If, over a long period of time, we ignore physical sensations, we eventually get to a point where our mind is so closed off we can no longer hear a word our body's saying.

It's about our fear of dependency too. What happens if we give in to illness? First, it means admitting we need someone else's help. We may have to tell a doctor about the problem and we might end up taking a prescription to the pharmacist. So that's already two people helping us. Then our partner, friends or relatives may also get to hear about our predicament and, if they care about us, they'll want to help too. They'll phone, visit, bring bunches of grapes or even tuck us up in bed. It can all seem too much for the chap who believes he should stand on his own two feet. After all, when did you last see Rambo waiting to see his doctor? He's usually far too busy arranging for other people to see theirs.

This detachment from our bodies is a real loss. You've probably noticed that Daleks look pretty miserable most of the time, and who can blame them, with a body made out of old rubbish bins and drain plungers? As humans, we've a body that's highly complex, multi-functioning but above all highly sensitive and alive. To cut ourselves off from our body's sensations is to miss out on one of our most important and **151** enjoyable senses. Learning to let go and get back in touch with our body can be a powerful, liberating experience.

Understanding, knowing and enjoying our bodies is all well and good, but there's an even more important aspect to being in touch with our physical side – our health. When our body talks to us, it wants to tell us something, and it doesn't normally joke around. We feel pain or fall ill because something's going wrong, and just trying to soldier on regardless is only likely to make things worse. Tension in the shoulders or a bout of flu, let alone a heart attack, might be telling us that we're putting ourselves under too much pressure, eating the wrong foods, not taking enough exercise or smoking and drinking too much.

Listening to these symptoms can encourage us to adjust to a less stressful workload and a healthier lifestyle. Ignoring them, on the other hand, can take us in the direction of greater pressure and greater ill health. Men who carry on as before after heart attacks may feel they're 'manfully' in control once more, but the chances are it won't be for long. This detachment from the body may be part of the reason why the life expectancy of the average man is almost six years lower than that of women (women born between 1985 and 1990 are expected to live 78.1 years and men 72.4 years).

In fact, when it comes to health, men have few claims to superiority. The statistics are startling and bleak. Twice as many men die before the age of 65 than women and almost three times as many men aged 15–64 die of coronary heart

disease. Lung cancer kills twice as many men as women and

prostate cancer kills three times more males than cervical cancer kills females. Men are three times more likely to die from an accident or violence and four times more likely to commit suicide.

If we're separated from our body, we're less likely to respect it and take good care of it. Maybe that's why men have higher levels of drinking and drug abuse than women, and also why we're more likely to indulge in dangerous pursuits such as bungee-jumping or joy-riding. However, if we see our body as a friend and an integral part of ourselves, we probably won't feel too great about stuffing it full of biscuits, burgers and beer.

# getting to know me

Fortunately, there are ways of recovering a sense of our own body. Try these:

## body awareness exercises

Find a quiet space where you can be warm and comfortable. Lie down on your back and close your eyes. Spend five to ten minutes just noticing your body's sensations. Start with your toes and work slowly up. How do the different muscles/ joints/skin/organs feel? Is there any tension or discomfort anywhere? Try touching your body with the tips of your fingers and be aware of how that feels. Using the phrase 'Now I am aware of . . . ' could help: 'Now I am aware of my toes itching . . . now I am aware of my left shoulder aching . . . **153** now I am aware of wanting to go to the toilet . . . '


## exercise

For many of us, the last time we did anything energetic was on the school playing field. If we're now couch potatoes whose idea of strenuous activity is heading for the kitchen for another plate of chips, then we should remember that exercise can serve as a reminder of the value of our body, as well as keeping us fit and healthy. (It's been claimed that physical inactivity creates the same health risk as smoking a packet of cigarettes a day.) Even if football or rugby doesn't appeal, there are many other physical activities to try, even if some of them may sound a bit 'woosie': squash, badminton, swimming, working out with weights, aerobics, dance. Whatever the choice, it's possible to use exercise more as a means of feeling and staying healthy than to take part in competitions or obsessively develop muscle. Someone who is currently sedentary will benefit from simply accumulating 30 minutes of moderate physical activity a day – and that includes taking the stairs rather than the lift and walking rather than driving to the station, as well as putting on some shorts and having a jog. Exercise also makes us feel better – its mood-elevating effect has even been shown to relieve depression.

## improving our diet

The more we understand about nutrition, and the more we think about what we eat, the more aware we can become of our body and how it responds to what we put in it. This doesn't mean that we all have to become macrobiotic vegans or never eat another flame-grilled Whopper. Rather, it means cutting down on the nasty fats (especially fried foods, full-fat dairy products and fatty meats) and eating more complex carbohydrates (pasta, bread, cereals, potatoes and rice). It's thought that the estimated average energy requirement for men is 2,500 kilocalories a day: no more than 20–30 per cent of these calories should come from fat, about 15 per cent should come from protein and the remaining 60–70 per cent from carbohydrate. As for booze, we can still imbibe as long as we're swigging no more than the recommended 21 units a week (equivalent to about 10–11 pints of beer, 2 litres of wine or two-thirds of a bottle of spirits). The World Health Organization also recommends that we eat about 1 pound of fruit and veg a day (excluding potatoes) – that's about five portions, each equivalent in size to an apple. The vitamins can help protect against heart disease and cancer and the fibre will do wonders for our haemorrhoids.

## massage

There's much more to massage than we'll find in a seedy sex parlour in an alley off the local high street. A proper massage aims to relax the body and to restore energy levels by **155** stimulating through pressure various muscle groups, especially in the neck, shoulders and back. Having a massage can help put us directly in touch with our body, particularly if we concentrate on the physical sensations as it's going on. Going to a professional masseur can be expensive, but it's easy for partners or friends to learn how to massage each other through a book or a massage course. As well as being relaxing, sharing a massage with a partner can also help to create more intimacy and closeness.

## yoga

This is more than physical exercise; in fact, yoga aims to combine physical strength and suppleness with spiritual awareness, deep relaxation, concentration and mental clarity. It stretches all parts of the body and is even supposed to massage the internal organs. We don't need to be a contortionist or even particularly fit to get started and we won't have to spend too much time lying on a bed of nails. It's possible to learn the basic postures from a book, but it's better to have a trained teacher. Most areas now have yoga evening classes where you can learn quite cheaply.

## alexander technique

This is a method of 're-educating' the body's posture so that it's in correct alignment. Advocates of the Alexander

156 Technique claim that although we were born knowing how to

stand, move and sit correctly, over time we've learnt many bad habits which have unbalanced our posture and pre-disposed us to illness and malfunction. It's claimed that the Alexander Technique can alleviate many mental and emotional as well as physical complaints, including backache, although we don't have to have any particular symptoms to learn it. Indeed, it may help prevent certain problems arising in the future. Alexander Technique can't be learnt from a book; it has to be taught, usually one-to-one, and this does mean it can be expensive.

## finding out more about our body

The more we know about the body's internal workings, the better we'll be able to relate to them. Given that, according to a recent MORI survey, only one in ten men can correctly identify the prostate gland on a diagram of the male body and that half of men believe prostate cancer can affect women too, there's clearly a need for us to educate ourselves better. Unless we're a hypochondriac, reading general health books can be a good place to start and, in the last few years, several good guides to men's health have been published. We can also weigh ourselves regularly to check whether we're too heavy for our height – if our waist exceeds a trouser-stretching 40 inches, we're almost certainly obese and need to cut out the jam doughnuts now – and check our pulse rate to make sure it's not too high. (70 beats a minute is about right for the averagely fit man at rest; the fitter we are, the lower our pulse.) **157**

The rest of this chapter will also take a closer look at some key parts of the male body and what can go wrong with them.

# a load of . . .

Men seem to have mixed feelings about their testicles. On the one hand, they're seen as a bit of a joke – we put down stupid ideas as 'a load of bollocks'; tease other men when they're hit in the 'goolies'; and enjoy comic strips like Viz magazine's 'Buster Gonad and his Unfeasibly Large Testicles'. At the same time, however, the balls are seen as the source of men's power, authority and masculinity. Brave men are said to have 'a lot of balls', while wimps are described as 'emasculated'. Perhaps it's not too surprising that powerful women are sometimes called 'ball-breakers'.

The testicles, extraordinarily complex organs, perform a variety of important functions. They not only produce several hundred million sperm a day (if they're in normal working order), but also testosterone, the hormone that stimulates the growth of body hair and muscles. Our testicles dangle precariously between our legs because human sperm cannot be produced at normal body temperature – the scrotum is an all-important 4–7° centigrade cooler than the rest of the body.

# the big C

One of the least-known health problems men can face is

testicular cancer. In fact, it's the most common of cancers in

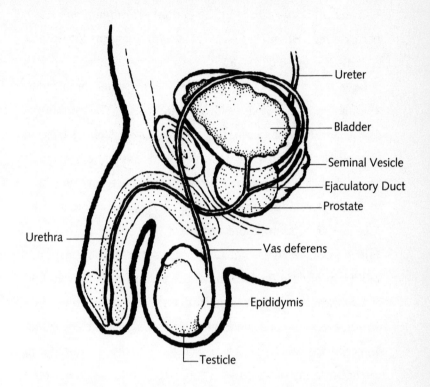

Ureter

Bladder

Seminal Vesicle

Ejaculatory Duct

Prostate

Urethra

Vas deferens

Epididymis

Testicle

**Your genitourinary system: how it all fits together**

young men and is the fourth most frequent killer of men aged 15–34 – those who least expect to be hit by serious illness. About 1 male in 450 can expect to develop it. Those at greatest risk are men who've had an undescended testicle – the risk is even higher if both testicles failed to descend. No-one is exactly sure why, but testicular cancer has become much more common in the last 50 years. One theory is that environmental pollutants and foodstuffs (particularly cow's milk) containing oestrogen have affected the development of the male while still in his mother's womb.

There are two main types of tumour – a seminoma (which mostly affects 30–40-year-olds) and a teratoma (mostly affecting 20–30-year-olds). The affected testicle is almost always removed, but seminomas are usually also treated with radiotherapy and teratomas with chemotherapy. Chemotherapy can be used for seminomas if the cancer has spread beyond the testicles. The loss of one testicle doesn't affect a man's physical ability to have or enjoy sex, but there may well be a temporary or long-term loss of fertility. Sperm banks can be used to store sperm before treatment.

The good news is that testicular cancer usually responds well to treatment, with over 90 per cent of men surviving in cases treated early. Removed testicles can also be replaced by often undetectable silicone gel implants which, unlike earlier implants, do not have the unfortunate quality of floating in the bath. Many men, however, through embarrassment, fear, squeamishness, ignorance or sheer self-neglect, put themselves at greater risk by waiting too long before seeing a doctor. About half of all cases are undetected until the tumour has spread to other organs. Even if this does happen, however, the outlook can still be good.

Because the sooner a testicular tumour is diagnosed, the more likely a cure will follow, it's a good idea for all men to carry out a regular monthly self-examination. It only takes a minute or two, and it could end up saving your life. Here's what you do:

- Wait until you've had a warm bath or shower. The heat relaxes the testicles, making them easier to check.

- Support the scrotum in the palm of the hand and note the size and weight of the testicles. It is common to have one testicle slightly larger or hanging lower than the other, but any noticeable increase in size or weight may indicate that something is wrong.

- Examine each testicle in turn. Using both hands, gently roll the testicle between the thumbs and fingers. Normally, testicles have a smooth surface. Check for any lumps or irregular swellings. Also, check for any change in firmness.

- Don't mistake the epididymis for an unusual lump. This is a large irregular structure which stores and transports sperm. It lies along the top and back of the testicle, feels like a small bag of worms and can be readily separated from the testicle in a warm bath.

- Apart from a lump, other warning signs can include a general sensation of heaviness in the scrotum or a dull ache in the lower abdomen or groin. Few experience sharp pain in the testicle, but this can still be a symptom.

- Occasionally the tumour produces hormones that cause the breasts to swell or feel tender.

- If you do notice a problem, don't automatically assume the worst – there could be many other explanations – but do arrange to see your doctor as soon as possible. Your testicle will be examined – a procedure that's not normally **161** the MANual

*even uncomfortable, let alone painful – and if there's anything suspicious, you'll be asked to have an ultrasound and a blood test.*

## other nut cases

The odds are that any lump will actually be caused by one of the many other less serious conditions that can also affect the gonads:

- *A **hernia** can bulge down into the scrotum. Here, part of the bowel drops down the tube through which the testicle descended from the abdomen before birth. Hernias, if causing discomfort, can be eased by use of a surgical belt ('truss') or cured by surgery.*
- *For no detectable reason, some men develop a **hydrocele**. This is an accumulation of fluid which may severely distend the testicles; in one case, a surgeon found a hydrocele of 2.25 litres. Hydroceles can also be caused by another underlying problem, such as an inflammation, infection or even a tumour, so it's always best to get it checked. Doctors can drain the fluid, use antibiotics or surgery to treat the condition. It isn't life-threatening in itself (although it can be painful) and one man is known to have refused treatment because he thought his enlarged scrotum made him more attractive to women.*
- *A lump may also be caused by a **varicocele**. Like so many male health problems, this is little discussed despite the*

162

fact that more than one in ten men end up with one. It's
a collection of distended veins and is more common in
the normally lower-hanging left testicle. Surgery is only
necessary when there's pain or an infertility problem,
although recent research has raised doubts about
whether varicoceles do actually cause a fall in the sperm
count.

- A **spermatocele** isn't a sperm on a bicycle but a fluid-
  filled lump on the epididymis. Such lumps can range in
  size from a pea to larger than a golf ball. A cyst on the
  epididymis can have similar symptoms. Again, surgery is
  normally necessary only where there is discomfort.

- **Epididymo-orchitis** is a bacterial or viral infection of the
  epididymis causing swelling and tenderness (the testicle
  may be hot, red and swollen) or even a fever. Antibiotics
  are usually prescribed and it may be necessary to rest
  with the testicles ceremoniously raised on a towel placed
  between the legs. Ice packs may also be used.

- In one incredibly painful condition, known as a **torsion**,
  the testicle twists on its axis, cutting off the blood
  supply. This can happen if the testicle is knocked, but
  also for no obvious reason. If you experience sudden
  pain in your testicle – maybe with abdominal pain or
  even vomiting – head straight for the nearest casualty
  department. An emergency operation to save the
  testicle is the only treatment and the sooner it's done
  the better.

# firing blanks

When David's wife couldn't get pregnant, he assumed the problem was hers because he could get erections and produce the fluids. However:

> The doctors did some tests on her and then decided to have a look at me. When I had the sperm test I was confident and blasé about it all. I was only 27 and I honestly thought I was as virile as a bloody bull. Then I got the result.

It wasn't good news:

> When the doctor told me, 'You ain't firing the bullets son', I felt like I was in a hollow room. I was devastated. I had no live sperm, absolutely none. Apart from the deaths of my granddad and my father, that was probably the lowest point in my life. I can't describe the hurt I felt. I dealt with it all bloody disastrously. I couldn't cope. I was so hard on myself. I was a bastard to live with. I loved my wife dearly but I was so scared she'd reject me. I behaved totally irrationally. When I filled in a tax form that asked: 'Are you male or female?' I put a tick between the two boxes because I didn't think I was either.

David's relationship went from bad to worse:

> I didn't talk to my wife or anybody else about how I felt.

I shut off totally. I reckoned if people knew I wasn't really a man I'd be the butt of jokes.

The nightmare only ended when David and his wife were able to adopt children:

I'm able to look at the whole business in another way now. I've got two lovely kids who I'd never have met if I had children of my own. Now I reckon I'm better off as I am.

Most doctors used to agree with David: so long as a man could ejaculate, any problems with fertility were thought to belong to his female partner. Fortunately, this example of medical sexism has now been overturned: it's now recognized that as many as 1 in 20 men has a fertility problem and the male is responsible for 50 per cent of all infertility cases. One in ten couples are affected at some point in their lives. Infertility is defined as the failure to conceive after a year of unprotected intercourse.

Whether it's the man or the woman who's infertile, it can give rise to difficulties in any relationship. Many couples regard having children as a normal, even inevitable, part of the development of their relationship and a failure to produce progeny can raise doubts about their future together. Sex may become problematic, even an area of conflict. As was the case for David, men can also feel as if their masculinity has been thrown into doubt. They may equate their fertility with a sense of potency and feel that if their sperm are not behaving like **165** jack-hammers then they're somehow lesser men.

To test for infertility, doctors will normally carry out a semen analysis. Unfortunately, this requires masturbation into a glass jar – not necessarily a pleasant experience, particularly when undertaken in a hospital toilet. Average sperm counts have been falling steadily over the past 50 years – possibly for the same reasons underlying the increase in testicular cancers. As yet, however, most men still have a more than adequate 20 to 200 million sperm per millilitre of semen and over 60 per cent of their sperm will be normally shaped and vigorously swimming in a straight line. By contrast, infertile men are likely to have a low sperm count (below 20 million per millilitre), with many dead or abnormal sperm and a high number swimming lazily around in circles.

Low sperm counts can have a number of causes, many of which are reversible. For example, there may be too much heat around the testicles because of tight underclothes, obesity or working conditions. Poor general health because of a bad diet or too much alcohol may also be responsible. Smoking and emotional stress can be a factor. Varicoceles may be a cause in up to 40 per cent of cases, although this is controversial. Infertility can also result from hormonal imbalances. A few men are infertile because they are born without a vas deferens and are therefore effectively in the position of men who have had a vasectomy. Infertility may also have resulted from mumps occurring after puberty – although this usually only affects one testicle – or treatment for testicular cancer.

Some cases of infertility can be treated quite simply by

wearing boxer shorts or even dipping the scrotum in a bowl of cold water three times a day (seriously). Sperm counts can also be increased by laying off the cigarettes and marijuana. Varicoceles can be repaired by straightforward surgery. Some doctors advocate the use of large daily doses of vitamin C, which may help to neutralize the naturally occurring antibodies that damage sperm, and extra vitamin E could help the process where the sperm binds to the egg. Drug treatments can also be used to tackle hormonal problems and, in some cases, it's possible for doctors to select a healthy sperm and inject it directly into the egg.

In a surprising 1 per cent of cases, doctors find that the suspected infertility is actually due to 'non-consummation' – where the couple don't realize that they're not having 'proper' intercourse. In cases where male infertility cannot be success-fully treated, many couples decide to try artificial insemination by an unknown donor using sperm from a sperm bank. Most men seem to be able to accept this – it's not as if their partner's having an affair, after all – but others find the challenge to their masculine potency harder to come to terms with.

## the best leg of three

Although most of us handle our penis regularly throughout the day – and put it to a variety of important uses – we probably give it surprisingly little thought. In fact, on closer inspection, the penis is a pretty extraordinary organ. Contrary to popular belief, it contains no muscle or bone; it is essentially **167** a lump of flesh and blood capable of prodigious expansion during sexual arousal. This happens when blood becomes trapped in three sponge-like cylinders along the length of the shaft. The penis is also versatile, carrying both semen and urine to the outside world, although fortunately, not at the same time.

## there's a lot of it about

Given all the recent attention on HIV and AIDS, you might be forgiven for thinking that other sexually transmitted diseases (STDs) had ceased to exist or were no longer important. In fact, they remain widespread – an estimated 350,000 plus men catch an STD each year. Unlike HIV, most other STDs are not life-threatening, but they do tend to be far more contagious and can cause severe pain and discomfort. If they remain untreated, they can lead to serious illness and sometimes even death. The main STDs, their symptoms and treatment are as follows:

- **Gonorrhoea:** *you'll notice a yellowish discharge from the tip of the penis and painful, frequent urination, often occurring three to five days after intercourse. If untreated through antibiotics, it can spread to the bladder, prostate and parts of the testicles, and lead to headaches, fever and possibly even infertility.*
- **Syphilis:** *usually around three weeks after infection – although it can be between 9 and 90 days – a painless,*

*dull red spot appears on the penis, which then ulcerates and forms a round or oval sore surrounded by a red rim. (Lesions may also be in the rectum or on the anus.) These primary symptoms disappear within four to six weeks, but if the bacteria are not treated with antibiotics, syphilis can ultimately lead to serious joint or heart problems, kidney or brain damage, liver disease and even death. It can also make your hair fall out.*

- **Non-specific urethritis (NSU):** *a thin and clear urethral discharge occurs 10–30 days after infection, often accompanied by painful urination. NSU is the most common STD, but it can be easily treated with antibiotics.*

- **Genital herpes:** *a few days after infection, localized burning feelings on the penis (and sometimes on the thighs, anus or buttocks) are followed by clusters of small, painful blisters. These burst after a few days and leave reddish wet sores or ulcers in their place. Most people also develop swollen glands in their groin, which can be very painful. The sores usually heal in a week or two, but the virus remains in the body. Infected people may suffer recurrent attacks, possibly accompanied by fever, headaches and muscle soreness. As yet there's no cure for herpes, although some drug treatments can reduce the severity of the symptoms.*

- **Pubic lice:** *an infestation of small, crab-like insects that live in pubic hair and feed off human blood. About five days after exposure, an infested person becomes*

169

intensely itchy in the pubic area, particularly at night. This can lead to scratching, redness and inflammation. Lice are treated by special creams, lotions or shampoo.

- **Genital warts:** *warts of a variety of shapes and sizes (but often looking like a tiny pink cauliflower) can be transmitted through sex, and can appear on the penis, scrotum, or even inside the urethra. They are usually treated with special wart-destroying ointments (not the sort you can buy in your local pharmacy). If these don't work, other treatments include freezing or burning off the warts. Larger warts may require surgical removal.*

- **Balanitis:** *the tip of the penis becomes red, blotchy and itchy. This isn't actually an STD, or in itself a serious condition, but can be quite uncomfortable. It's normally caused by friction during sex or irritation from spermicides; some men who wear a condom find their own sperm act as an irritant if the condom is left on too long after sex. Once the skin has been damaged, it's at risk of infection.*

Keep an eye on your penis and, if you have any of the above symptoms, contact your doctor or a hospital genitourinary medicine (GUM) clinic. Just because the symptoms of an STD change or even disappear doesn't mean that the disease has somehow cured itself. It's worth remembering that if you practise safer sex to reduce the risks of transmitting HIV, you'll also reduce the risk of transmitting most other STDs. What's

more, if you do have an untreated STD, you could be more at

risk of transmitting, or catching, HIV. Most GUM clinics provide a routine check-up for STDs, even if you have no symptoms. If you are not monogamous, having an annual check has a lot to recommend it, for both your health and that of your partners. You could treat it as if you were going to the dentist for a regular check-up (with the added advantage that there's absolutely no danger of an electric drill going anywhere near your genitals). GUM clinics are completely confidential; in fact, you don't even have to give your name.


## roundheads or cavaliers?

Some adult men may need to be circumcized if their foreskins cannot be easily retracted – a condition known as *phimosis*, which can lead to infection of the head of the penis. However, most circumcisions are performed on babies at the request of their parents. The proportion of British males circumcized has fallen from 20 per cent in 1945 to under 5 per cent today, although virtually all Jewish and Moslem men have had their foreskins removed.

A father-to-be (whether Jewish, Moslem or of any other faith or none) who's considering circumcision may find it difficult to know what's best for his son, since the issue is surrounded by many myths. For example, it's often said that circumcized men are more attractive lovers, cleaner and less likely to pass on sexually transmitted diseases. However, these claims have been challenged in recent years and there are now thought to be few positive advantages to chopping off the 171 foreskin. While it's true that only uncircumcized men get cancer of the penis, this is in fact a very rare disease (accounting for just 100 deaths a year in England and Wales). Moreover, there's no longer any clear evidence that smegma – the white, cheesy secretion produced beneath the foreskin – increases the chances of cervical cancer in women.

And what do the psychologists have to say? Some believe that circumcision can lead to emotional and sexual problems in adult life. There can be little doubt that circumcision is a painful and traumatic event. Adults circumcized for medical reasons are sedated, while babies are usually not given even a local anaesthetic. Common sense suggests that circumcision in these circumstances must have some psychological impact, although this has to be weighed against the feelings of loss of, or exclusion from, his cultural identity that a Jewish or Moslem boy might feel if he wasn't circumcized. Most childcare experts now recommend that a young boy's penis be left intact.

## 'it's my prostrate, doctor'

Say that to your GP and they will almost certainly enjoy a private snigger because it's actually the pros*tate* gland. Like the testes, it's one of the few organs unique to males. However, despite the fact that most men will experience prostate troubles at some point in their lives, many seem to know very little about it. One MORI poll found that nine out of ten men knew the function of women's ovaries, while only three out of ten knew the function of their own prostate.

The prostate is about the size of a walnut and is located directly below the bladder. It surrounds the urethra (which carries urine from the bladder) at its junction with the vas deferens (which carries sperm from the testicles) and the ejaculatory duct (through which fluid passes from the seminal vesicles). The prostate produces an alkaline fluid which makes up about 20 per cent of the ejaculate. Enzymes secreted by the gland cause the seminal fluid to clot, helping the semen to stick to the cervical mucus. The prostate also has an important function as the valve which stops urine and sperm coming out at the same time. The prostate is a very sensitive organ which, when stimulated during sex either by a finger or penis through the anus, can produce an extremely powerful and pleasant sensation. Some men even find that prostate stimulation makes their semen shoot out further.

## the smaller the better

One of the most common prostate problems occurs when the gland starts to grow abnormally, sometimes to the size of a grapefruit. This can lead to problems with urination – indeed, one the first symptoms men often have of a prostate problem is a difficulty with passing water. The stream can become slow and hesitant and the bladder may not empty fully, requiring frequent trips to the toilet. This may be a particular problem at night. Men with prostate enlargement often have to rush to the toilet and, to their embarrassment, sometimes don't make it in time. Such men can end up planning their daily journeys **173** around a map of accessible lavatories.

Prostate enlargement can either be benign or cancerous. Most cases are benign, but because the early symptoms of both conditions are similar, any persistent 'waterworks' problem should be referred to a doctor. Unfortunately, too many men still seem to think that these sorts of problems are a natural and harmless by-product of ageing and so don't seek advice. In the United States, men over 40 are advised to have an annual prostate check-up. British men should consider asking their doctor for a check-up too, although doctors are currently divided about the advisability of screening for prostate cancer when there are no symptoms. Some believe detecting the early signs of cancer may cause needless anxiety, since the disease may only spread slowly and never become serious enough to require treatment. Early detection, therefore, may mean that many men will undergo unnecessary surgery.

However, prostate cancer is a major killer, closely following lung cancer in the death 'league table'. Over 14,000 men are diagnosed with it each year in Britain and almost 10,000 die. It mostly affects older men; in fact, virtually all men over 85 have at least microscopic signs of prostate cancer, although only 1 in 40 elderly men has any symptoms. The cause is unknown, although a diet rich in animal fats may be a factor, and men whose work exposes them to cadmium are known to run an increased risk. The disease tends to run in families and it's also possible that the cancer is somehow linked to testosterone, as

it never occurs in castrated men.

A doctor can often tell whether the enlargement is cancerous by feeling the prostate with a finger via the anus (don't attempt self-diagnosis!) This is commonly combined with a blood test, ultrasound and (in suspicious cases) a biopsy taken through the rectum. Treatment for an enlarged prostate will depend on its cause and, if it's cancerous, on the extent to which the disease has spread. Surgery is often recommended, during which part or all of the prostate is removed by means of a 'telescope' passed through the penis. Where there is cancer, radiotherapy or drugs to reduce testosterone production may also be used. Treatment may affect a man's sex life and he may experience dry orgasms – which can still be pleasurable, however – but sometimes it may cause chronic impotence.

## a little infection

Younger men can suffer from *prostatitis*, a bacterial inflammation of the prostate in which the pain is referred to nearby sites: perhaps to a testicle, the base or tip of the penis, or the perineum (the area between the testicles and the anus). There may also be a burning sensation during urination. In its acute form, prostatitis can lead to fever, chills and painful ejaculation. Chronic prostatitis has also been linked to blood in the ejaculate. It can usually be cured by antibiotics, although in some cases it may require prolonged treatment. On a more positive note, some doctors recommend more sex, since orgasm increases the prostate's blood supply, helping to flush out bacteria.

**175**

## not much on top

Men seem to have mixed feelings about baldness. For some –
film stars Telly Savalas or Yul Brynner, for example – it's a
symbol of toughness and virility. Sting has claimed his baldness
is 'sexy', and Captain Jean-Luc Picard is able to command the
Federation's premier Starship – and be considered one of the
most attractive men in the world – despite being a baldie. Most
men, however, seem to feel that being hirsutely challenged
reflects creeping old age and declining sexual powers. Julius
Caesar is reputed to have worn a laurel wreath not as a symbol
of his military genius but to hide his baldness. Even earlier, the
Egyptians are thought to have sought a cure for a thinning
pate. And today, many men go to great lengths to conceal
receding temples and increasingly visible crowns. Some grow
their remaining hair to prodigious lengths, attempting to
camouflage the more sparsely covered areas. Others use
toupees, resort to expensive hair transplants or quack potions
more likely to cause dermatitis than hair growth. Men who try
to convince themselves that their baldness is due to their
massive virility are also backing a loser – blood levels of
testosterone are usually normal in balding men.

All this behaviour isn't too surprising. The image of
the balding man is usually negative. In films or adverts, for
example, he's rarely seen with attractive women and is often
portrayed as slightly pathetic, unpopular and a bit of a loser.
The desirable male body of the 90s is definitely young, slim,
well-muscled and hairy on top. Psychological tests carried out

**176** by Goldsmiths College in London on 182 men aged 19–73 discovered big differences between men with no hair loss and men who were semi- or largely bald. The sparser the active follicles, the greater the loss of self-esteem, depression, introversion and feelings of being unattractive. The reality is that, for many men, balding is far from being a laughing matter.

The average healthy, fully haired bonce has some 125,000 hairs of which 80–100 are naturally lost daily. But progressive thinning is an inevitable part of life for most men and may begin to occur from the mid–20s. By the age of 50, some two-thirds of men are going bald and most 80-year-olds have very little on top. When men do go bald, two-thirds of men start thinning at the temples; the remainder start moulting on the crown.

More rapid baldness can also occur as a result of certain medical conditions. *Alopecia areata*, for example, results in the hair suddenly falling out in patches and may be associated with stress, although the hair usually grows back. This condition can affect men even in their teens and 20s. If the hair doesn't reappear, treatments include steroids applied to the scalp or ultraviolet light therapy. Prolonged ill health can also result in hair thinning, as can the side-effects of some prescribed drugs. In some cases of *alopecia totalis*, the whole scalp area becomes bald and the eyelashes and eyebrows may lose their hair too.

Recently, big claims have been made for the drug Minoxidil which, when massaged into the scalp twice a day, can reduce the rate of hair loss for most users and stimulate new hair growth for about one in three. However, only about 10 per **177** cent achieve a cosmetically good result, the treatment is expensive and slow and has to be continued indefinitely otherwise baldness will return. Electric scalp stimulation has also been promoted as another possible cure, but test results are inconclusive. Surgery to reduce the area of baldness or to implant artificial hair is not only costly and unpleasant but also of only short-term use: if your genes are determined you should be bald, your hair loss will continue regardless. You could end up with tufts of plastic hair surrounded by patches of exposed pate. Most baldies would probably be little worse off using the ineffective, but much cheaper, remedies of chilli peppers, cold tea or chicken droppings.

In cases where hair loss is natural, rather than resorting to such treatments, it might be preferable for us to think about why we're so bothered by baldness. Perhaps, like elegantly greying temples, baldness should be reinterpreted as a sign of increasing maturity rather than declining powers. Samson aside, the reality is that hair loss bears no relation whatsoever to any supposedly manly quality. It might be better if we judged ourselves and each other by what goes on *in* our heads, not on top of them. In the USA, an organization called the Bald-Headed Men of America even fights for 'bald liberation' – the right for men to be bald and proud of every single hair that they don't have.

# menopausal men

If you're over 35, you may well know how it feels. You wake up one morning wondering what it all means – life, that is, not quantum physics or surfing the Internet. You wonder whether you're doing the right job – because it now seems pretty boring and futile – and whether you have the right partner. You feel disappointed, bored and trapped. You think about the years ahead and wonder how you'll get through them. You worry about your steadily declining sexual powers – when you were 20 you easily managed three orgasms a night, now you're pushed to come up with one. 'So what state will my genitals be in by the time I'm 50?' you ask yourself bleakly. You notice that you're ogling much younger women and contemplating the possibility of an affair. You're also noticing younger men and envying their bodies, their energy and how easy it all seems for them. You feel tired, listless and even depressed. In short, you're confused and worried about your role in life and you don't know how to cope.

If you recognize these feelings, you're not alone. In fact, the numbers of men experiencing a so-called 'mid-life crisis' may actually be growing as the number of divorces rises and work becomes increasingly insecure. In a culture where youth is prized and to be old is to be seen as redundant, it's perhaps not surprising that middle age – a time of transition – is when we're likely to re-evaluate our lives. Moreover, since the real man is implicitly youthful – that's why the later *Star Trek* films with their ageing crew were seen as a bit of a joke – it's hard **179** for men to adjust to having a body which makes it harder and harder for them to appear manly.

However the mid-life crisis, while sometimes frightening or painful, can also be seen as an opportunity for us to review, and perhaps change, the direction of our lives. Some of us try to cope by drinking more, having affairs, paying for sex or even having cosmetic surgery to make us look younger. But we could also find ways to talk about how it feels to get older and the problems we experience.

One controversial new treatment is hormone replacement therapy (HRT). Some doctors now believe that many men, like all women, experience significant hormonal changes in middle age – this has even been dubbed the 'viropause' or 'endopause'. According to this theory, not all male mid-life crises have a hormonal explanation – some are purely psychological or emotional in origin – but many do. Affected men may experience certain physical symptoms which accompany, and probably reinforce, their angst. They include drier skin, decreasing body hair, reduced sexual desire and/or impotence, smaller quantities of ejaculate, night sweats, fatigue and irritability. One theory is that the viropause is caused by the body's increasing inability to utilize testosterone. It's not that the testosterone level falls; rather, it's affected by the body's increased production of another sex hormone (binding globulin) and the decreasing ability of cells to absorb testosterone as they thicken with age. The treatment is – as you've probably already guessed – to take a testosterone supplement.

180 Some men who've tried HRT claim that it has a dramatically

positive effect. Many doctors, however, are more cautious. First, they believe some men are too eager to seek a physical explanation for their anxieties; what they really need to do is to look more at how they feel about getting older and find a psychological solution to their unhappiness. Secondly, there are worries that extra testosterone can increase sexual desire but not necessarily the ability to perform, a scenario that can prove deeply frustrating. And, thirdly, and perhaps most seriously, testosterone is known to stimulate the spread of prostate cancer. If you still want to try HRT, you'll have to pay for it too – you're very unlikely to find an NHS doctor who'll prescribe it.

## asking for help

David, a 30-year-old teacher, usually gets flu about once a year and it knocks him out completely for four or five days:

> I live on my own and I usually don't tell anybody I'm ill until I'm almost better. I suppose I don't want them to see me looking a mess and feeble. I don't want them to feel obliged to look after me. I guess I also start doubting whether they really like me. I have visions of them groaning down the phone and halfheartedly dragging themselves round to see me with a withered bunch of grapes.

But last time he got flu, David tried something different:

I decided to contact my friends straight away. My best friend came round the same evening and spent about two hours with me. He cooked me some supper and we chatted and watched TV together. He phoned me up twice the next day to see how I was and other friends dropped in to see me too. I felt very uncomfortable, but overall definitely better for the human contact. I also made sure I stayed in bed for that extra day. Normally, I'd get up and try to go back to work still feeling pretty awful. This time, I continued resting even though I felt I should get up. It's difficult to say how much it helped, but I think I did get over the illness more quickly. I also felt as if I was treating myself better and I felt good about that.

David's story illustrates one more step we need to take to ensure that we have a healthy body – feeling OK about asking for advice, help and treatment when we need it.

Seeing a doctor can be an essential first step to recovery, and having friends and relatives around can cheer us up and keep our morale going. What's more, asking others for help can alleviate some of the more practical pressures of being ill: we can ask them to do some shopping, cook a few meals, or even provide a much-needed massage. Those of us with more serious conditions may find it useful to join one of the self-help groups that exist for fellow sufferers. Talking to others about our illness and sharing feelings may help us to come to terms with it, feel less alienated from other people and give us a belief that the disease is conquerable.

We can even ask for help with our health when we're actually feeling healthy. Women have been having preventive health checks for years and, more recently, they've started to be introduced for men. Many doctors, and some private health clinics, now run Well-Man or Well-Person clinics where you can have your weight, blood pressure, urine, cholesterol, testicles and even prostate gland checked for potential problems. These services can also help to improve our general knowledge and awareness of our health: a study of an Oxfordshire Well-Man clinic found that many of the men attending had improved their diet, increased their exercise levels and drank or smoked less.

Health doesn't concern real men. They can smoke, drink, take drugs, stay up all night and eat junk food without even getting so much as an upset stomach. They're as likely to get ill as Arnold Schwarzenegger is to have a baby. Although he may spend hours perfecting a body made up of slabs of taut muscle, the real man probably knows less about a healthy lifestyle than your local fish and chip shop knows about a low-fat diet. But men don't have to die young in ignorance. Good information is now widely available – all that needs to change is our attitude. If we can begin to realize that we don't have to prove we're a real man by ignoring and neglecting our health, we can start to get in touch with our body and listen to what it's telling us. This may be uncomfortable at times – it may mean playing squash is off the agenda while we're getting over flu, deleting burgers from the daily menu, checking our **183** testicles for lumps and even asking for help when we're ill. But as complete men, we'll have a better sense of our body – we'll no longer see it just as a collection of separate parts – and we'll also be healthier and able to enjoy our life for longer.

# work:
# the fulfilled man

## who's that man?

You're standing by the drinks table at a party. Someone comes up to you, chats for a few minutes and then asks, 'What do you do?' Would you say that you love watching American football, spend your Sundays gardening or enjoy cooking lasagne? Probably not. You'd be more likely to reply that you're a brain surgeon, a teacher, an electrician or unemployed. Our working life really does seem central to the way we define our identity – to others as well as ourselves.

But why is that? It's probably because it's assumed that men's main role in society is to be the worker and breadwinner, the modern equivalent of the hunter and protector. From an early age, boys are told that their future job will be the most important thing in their life. Although attitudes are changing, boys are still more likely than girls to be asked, 'What do you want to be when you grow up?' And you don't get many points for saying 'a father' or 'happy'. What adults are expecting – and what they usually hear – is 'I want to be a train driver' or 'I'd like to make lots of money.' Boys are taught to see their future selves as their **185** future jobs. The two are synonymous.

When MORI asked 800 men aged 18–45 who they most admired, 25 per cent put Richard Branson at the top of their list. He scored more highly than any other potential role model. The real man is clearly powerful and successful. We're more likely to aspire to be a man like *Dynasty*'s Blake Carrington or *Dallas*'s J R Ewing – with a fleet of stretch limos, big offices and beautiful wives – than someone who stacks shelves in the local supermarket or is unemployed. We may also admire jobs requiring physical prowess. Many of us are fascinated with the shadowy men of the Special Air Service, or revere sportsmen like Eric Cantona and Linford Christie. Batman scores doubly high in the real-man league table: he's strong and athletic while his alter ego, Bruce Wayne, is a company chief executive. All these men are appreciated primarily because of their work – we don't, after all, love Cantona just for his philosophical ramblings.

All this can easily provide a very narrow sense of self-identity. When we define ourselves primarily by our work, the fact that we might be a caring father or a good friend becomes peripheral. We end up sidelining, or at least minimizing, whole chunks of our identity. It's as if a large part of us doesn't exist or have very much meaning or value. If we hate our work, or if we don't work at all, defining ourselves through a job can be particularly destructive. It's no wonder that men who are unemployed often go through periods of anxiety and severe depression. Being made redundant can feel worse than being rejected by a lover. Failing at work means failing as a man.

Even retirement can be very painful for men, reflected in the fact that many fall ill or die soon afterwards.

## all work, no play

Another very good reason why we tend to define ourselves through work may simply be the amount of time spent doing it. If we're up first thing in the morning to go to work and get home last thing at night, there really isn't an opportunity to identify with much else – especially if the rest of our time is spent either commuting to work, recovering from it or worrying about it. Incredibly, despite talk of 'the leisure society', the number of hours spent at work is actually rising. It's been said that modern company strategy is to halve the number of people employed, work them twice as hard and hope they'll be three times as effective. As job insecurity rises, moreover, many employees need little encouragement to work long hours to keep their jobs.

One in eight British managers now works more than 60 hours a week and more than half take work home during the week, according to the think-tank Demos. A quarter of all British male employees work more than 48 hours a week and nearly a fifth of unskilled and manual workers toil for more than 50 hours. For many, work encroaches into the evenings, cutting down social time, or even extends into the night, cutting down sleeping time. It's almost as if organizations are now suffering from 'presenteeism' rather than absenteeism, with many staff at work when they really should be at home. **187**

For some of us, work has become a virtual addiction, where we feel compelled to work virtually every hour available. When the *Financial Times* newspaper surveyed 1,250 managers, it found that over half said work took priority over everything else in their lives.

Putting so much emphasis on our work inevitably means that we simply have much less time to devote ourselves to other activities – relationships, contact with children, friendships, social life, cultural activities. If we find our work boring, frustrating, stressful, or even just plain OK, then we can end up without much of a life. One ironic implication of working long hours is that it often makes people less rather than more effective – those who work very hard often get jaded and the 'rounded' worker (the one with a so-called 'hinterland' of other interests) actually has much more to offer than the workaholic. One reason why employers often find women to be more efficient and effective workers, particularly at management level, is that they're much more likely than men to have a variety of interests outside of work.

Are you a workaholic, whether through choice or necessity? One way of finding out whether work is dominating your life is to ask yourself the following:

- *Do you regularly bring work home or do you often work in your free time?*
- *Do you work more than 50 hours a week on average?*
- *Do you often work during your lunch breaks or miss out lunches altogether?*

- *Do you get complaints from your partner or friends about how much time you spend on work?*
- *Do you feel that you're missing out on other parts of your life – perhaps spending time with your children or partner, sport or exercise, cultural activities – because of the amount of time and energy you devote to work?*
- *Do you feel bored, guilty, or at a loose end when you're not working?*
- *Do you have few interests outside of work?*
- *If your boss asked you to attend an important meeting after you'd already arranged to take your partner out for her birthday, would you turn down your partner rather than disappoint your boss?*
- *If you had to describe yourself in one word, would it be your occupation?*
- *Are the major goals in your life work-related?*

If you have answered 'yes' to three or more questions, then you may have workaholic tendencies. If you answered 'yes' to six or more questions, then workaholism could well be an issue seriously worth thinking about.

## the greasy pole

Because many men's sense of self-worth is so intimately linked to the nature of their work, the struggle to succeed can become more than just a quest for a better job – it's a battle for self-validation. A man at the bottom of the office hierarchy **189** doesn't just want to reach the top for the shiny new office, the swivel chair and the proverbial key to the executive washroom. He wants to get there so that he can feel good about himself and so that others will approve of him. When the polling organization Gallup quizzed 1,000 men aged 20–45, 80 per cent said earning the respect of colleagues at work and friends mattered 'a lot' or 'quite a lot'. If he's at the bottom of the hierarchy, a man may neither respect himself, nor think others respect him. It may even be emotionally painful for him to be there – the sooner he can climb the ladder of success, the better.

The struggle for success is also a battle to gain power – one of the key aims of the inner Arnie. Imagine, for instance, that you're the chief executive of a fast-food corporation. Just think of how many thousands of people you can push around. Not just your personal secretary and your board of directors, but everyone down to the guy working at the take-out counter in the local high street branch. At any time, you could wander down for a milkshake, complain it tastes like chemical sludge and fire him on the spot. You'd certainly feel more manly than your lowly employee. First, he's persistently harassed by his supervisor to speed up his work. Then he's fired for something which is beyond his control. Being pushed around makes most men feel de-masculinized. It's a sign of submissiveness, not of being in control.

The chances are that being successful also means we earn more money. On the most basic level, this ensures that we can

improve our quality of life: holidays in Barbados rather than

Benidorm; lobster, not tinned tomato soup; soft instead of hard toilet paper. But a greater cash flow also increases our status as a real man. First, because it means we'll be better providers and protectors for a family, if we have one. Secondly, because money bestows power. Cash means we can do what we want, buy what we want, go where we want. Being rich means not being pushed around. We're the ones in charge. And more money can also make us feel that we've got greater 'pulling' power when it comes to desirable women – let's face it, supermodel Claudia Schiffer's unlikely to go out with anyone earning less than the national average. Not surprisingly, earning a lot of money matters 'a lot' or 'quite a lot' to almost three-quarters of men, according to the Gallup survey.

Being successful also means that we can leave something behind after we've gone. Women, as mothers, have traditionally seen children as their legacy. But because men are generally less involved in parenting, we frequently feel a need to look elsewhere to leave our mark. By writing a best-selling screenplay, founding a business empire or designing an award-winning building, we feel we can transcend our finite existence. It seems to give our life some meaning and direction. More than that, it suggests that we can continue to be powerful even when we're dead.

Success can be so enticing that some men sacrifice everything else in their life to try to achieve it. Instead of enjoying what we're doing when we're doing it, we spend our time worrying about whether we're going to make it or whether we're doomed to remain on the lower echelons. We may even **191** spend years doing jobs that we don't enjoy to work our way up, or else make career choices based on what has better prospects rather than what we actually like doing. A teacher, for instance, may find himself moving to an administrative post because he wants to climb the hierarchy and earn more money, whereas in his heart he knows that contact with pupils is what he really loves.

All this might be worthwhile if success brought happiness, but the truth is that it rarely does. Our struggle to succeed may well be little more than an attempt to fill a gaping hole of male insecurity. Trying to fill this hole with success can often provide some temporary satisfaction, but ultimately the hole is always going to be there for as long as we feel the need to live up to the unrealistic goals of the inner Arnie. We might be far better off looking at where the hunger for success comes from and perhaps finding other, and more permanent, ways of getting our needs met.

The struggle for success can also be more destructive than constructive in the workplace. True, it might encourage people to work harder to reach the top but, at the same time, it can introduce an unhealthy degree of conflict which affects the quality of work. Two people on the same rung of the ladder, for instance, may avoid cooperating with each other for fear that the other may jump them in the hierarchy. Meanwhile, feelings of resentment and jealousy may stop those at the 'bottom' working efficiently with those at the 'top'; conversely, feelings of superiority may stop those in charge really taking seriously what those 'beneath' them have to say.

# danger, men at work

Throughout history, men have generally taken on the most dangerous work. These days, we might not be hunting dinosaurs to earn the admiration of a loin-clothed Raquel Welch, but men's work is still fraught with the possibilities of injury and even death. The vast majority of soldiers, construction workers, miners and oil riggers are male, so it's not surprising that an overwhelming nine out of every ten fatal injuries at work happen to men, as do three-quarters of all major injuries.

While non-manual workers are at less risk of serious physical injuries, different kinds of dangers still lurk at their workplaces. Even computers, introduced to make work easier and more efficient, can cause a wide range of health problems, from eyestrain to skin rashes to repetitive strain injury. Perhaps the most serious problem facing the modern worker, however, is stress. Stress can be caused by a number of different factors: fear of being unable to cope with an insurmountable workload and too many responsibilities; a feeling of being trapped in a job and unable to break out; or even (strangely, perhaps) boredom, not having enough control over work and not being sufficiently challenged. What's more, almost every worker now has to live with the fear of redundancy and most of us are under continual pressure to work more flexibly, learn new skills and adapt to the ever-changing demands of the labour market.

Despite the health risks of work, many of us refuse to take them seriously. If we're asked to do something dangerous, we often put on a facade of manly bravado and pretend that 193 we're not worried at all. How many of us have done our backs in from trying to carry a filing cabinet up three flights of stairs? How many of us have worked all day on a computer without a break and left work with sore eyes and a splitting headache? A lot of men seem almost actively to enjoy putting themselves under immense pressure to show how much they can take before they collapse. (The Japanese, who work the longest hours in the industrialized world, suffer 10,000 deaths a year from what they dub *karoshi* – overwork.) On the other hand, men who argue for better safety regulations, or who deal with stress by taking time off, are often derided as wimps. We can easily end up trying to prove our competence by denying the health risks that come with the job rather than by finding ways of tackling what's actually causing those risks. Even trade unionists – traditionally a very manly bunch – have tended to regard health and safety problems as secondary to the 'central' issues of power, pay and holidays.

## that's for girls

Kevin, now 38 and a clinical nurse manager, started working as a nurse when he was 21. Before this he'd been working for British Steel, but had always wanted to be a nurse, even as a little boy:

I got another job first because I didn't think there were such things as male nurses. It never dawned on me that I really could be a nurse. In the Welsh Valley where I lived, no way would a man become a nurse. But after I had a row with my boss, I just left my job, went to the local Job Centre and said I wanted to become a nurse. I had an interview a few days later and I was accepted for the training.

Even then, however, it wasn't easy for Kevin:

My father, who was a miner, didn't speak to me while I was training. He thought it was a totally unacceptable job because it was women's work. The only time he did speak to me, he got very angry and said, 'What the hell are you doing in a nurse's job – that's a poof's job. You're no son of mine.' I think he felt ashamed. But I've never regretted my decision and I've always enjoyed nursing.

How would you fancy being a nurse? OK, so you might not like the idea of dressing up in one of those white outfits with a 'funny' hat, but what probably puts most men off even more is that nursing is still often seen as 'women's work'. It's something many men would find too embarrassing to consider for themselves or, in the case of Kevin's father, for their sons. Like him, we might well think that only men who are not 'proper' men (i.e. gay) would be interested in doing 'women's work'. That's certainly an assumption commonly made about male ballet dancers, secretaries and hairdressers.

Jobs such as bricklayer, footballer, car salesman or airline pilot are certainly more securely located at the masculine end **195** of the 'male/female axis' – along which most occupations can be placed. When we come to choosing jobs, the 'male-ness' or 'female-ness' of a career can sometimes influence – albeit unawarely – our decision. For instance, we may end up teaching geography rather than domestic science because it's seen as more manly and therefore appropriate. That's OK if we prefer geography, but if we actually like domestic science more, our perception of how manly a job is can prevent us doing what we really want.

Defining jobs along a male/female axis also has important repercussions for women. If jobs 'x' and 'y' are reserved for men, then it can mean that women have little option but to do job 'z'. And you can guarantee that job 'z' is almost certainly less prestigious and well paid than jobs 'x' and 'y'. Women's jobs have tended to be the most repetitive and unskilled, generally consisting of the so-called '10 Cs': catering, cleaning, clerking, cashiering, counter minding, clothes-making, clothes-washing, coiffure, child minding, and care of the sick. While a growing number of women are now belatedly moving into the 'male' professions, there's often still an underlying suspicion that women aren't really up to the job. Such prejudice can both unfairly hinder women from getting on in the world of work and also stop organizations from hiring the best 'man' for the job – often a woman.

# man about the house

Another job well over to the 'female' end of the male/female work axis is that of houseworker. (In fact, there's not yet a widely understood alternative word for 'housewife', reinforcing the way this role is seen as exclusively female.) Many men shiver at the mere thought of being a 'house husband'. And it's worse than just having to wave a feather duster around. If a man was a house-husband, he'd be dependent on his partner to provide for him financially. Being in such a position of vulnerability and powerlessness can raise the hairs on the back of even the newest man's neck.

Even when it's not a full-time occupation, many men shirk at the idea of doing housework. When market researchers Mintel surveyed 1,500 adults, they found that just 1 per cent of couples shared domestic chores equally. The Central Statistical Office has also found that while DIY is done mainly by men in eight out of ten households, every other domestic chore is done mainly by women. This is despite the fact that a majority of men and women say that they believe most tasks should be shared equally. Even when women have a full-time job, they are often still doing most of the cooking and clean-ing. This could, in part, be due to the way men see housework as wimpy, but there's probably also another, more straightfor-ward reason – men simply hate doing it.

Women probably hate it too, of course, but most have been brought up to see housework as their responsibility. That's why they tend to feel compelled to do it while we watch television or go out for a game of squash. It's very easy, in this situation, 197 to justify our lack of activity by saying things like 'She's better at it than me', 'Well, I cleaned the car last month' or 'I need to sort out my childhood traumas before I can challenge my sexist behaviour.' We could instead ask ourselves whether our behaviour is really fair and consider how the relationship might be improved if we became more involved in housework. We may even be surprised to find some of it satisfying. Cooking, for instance, offers opportunities to be adventurous and creative, much more so than the washing-up, a task many more men are prepared to do.

## career directions

'I've always felt as if I should get a good job and be successful at it,' says Mark, 35 and currently unemployed. His parents encouraged him to do his homework so that he'd get good exam results and go to university. And when he got there, he felt as if he should work hard to get a good degree, which he duly did:

But I never really enjoyed being a student – I always felt like I didn't quite know why I was there or what the point of it all was. After I got my degree, I started a teacher-training course, but I didn't really want to be a teacher and I left after a term and got a manual job in a factory.

Mark was then again seized by the urge to succeed and 198 eventually got a 'proper' job with the local council. He was now being paid good money and was soon able to afford to buy a house with his girlfriend. But:

> After three years, I started to get bored and began to think things like, 'Well, I'm 28 now and I can't stay on this rung of the ladder forever.' I felt as if I had to move up so, when my boss left, I applied for her job and got it. At first, I was delighted. I had more money and power: I was responsible for supervising the work of eight people and running an office. But the stress half-killed me. I kept on getting ill and having to take time off. I especially hated having to confront my staff and get them to do things they didn't want to do. After two years, I left. In fact, I'd come to hate it so much, I resigned without another job to go to. I've now been unemployed for five months and I'm still not sure what I want to do instead.

As Mark has discovered, it's often easier to decide that we don't like a job than to know what we would like. Choosing a different career path is never easy. Indeed, in the midst of a recession, it can be a bit like playing Russian roulette. If we're going to spend most of our lives working, however, we may as well try to do something we enjoy. It can be extremely difficult to acknowledge that our job, or how we're doing it, isn't really what we want – that it's more what we feel we *ought* to be doing – especially if we've invested a large amount of our life in following a particular path. But the sooner we admit it the better, because then we can start making some changes. **199**

If you're not certain about what you're doing, there are several questions you could consider:

- *What kinds of work do you honestly enjoy?*
- *What kinds of work do you honestly dislike?*
- *If you could do any job, what would it be? What's stopping you from doing it?*
- *Is the desire to be manly affecting your choice of work? Are you refusing to consider jobs that seem to you more suitable for women?*
- *What level of income do you need or want?*
- *What sort of physical conditions do you want to work in (outdoors, in an office, a job with a lot of travelling, for example)?*
- *Do you want to be able to work independently, as part of a team or in a more rigid hierarchy?*
- *How do you want to be managed? Do you want to be a manager and, if so, at what level?*
- *What level of job security do you want?*
- *Are all your goals work-related? What else do you want to achieve in life?*

If we're thinking about changing career, but find these questions difficult to resolve on our own, we might find it useful to see a careers counsellor. Careers counsellors generally operate differently from the kind of therapists who can help with emotional issues. They will tend to see clients for just a few sessions, focus on feelings and attitudes to work and probably conduct various aptitude tests. Once a possible area of work has been agreed on, the counsellor can then give practical advice about employers and the best way to apply for jobs or any training that might be needed.

We may also decide that we need to think about how we classify jobs as 'male' or 'female'. If we'd really like to work with children, for example, but feel that it would be too embarrassing or humiliating, then we might find it useful to talk to other men who already do that sort of work. We could ask them how they feel about it and find out if they really do get humiliated by others. The chances are, put-downs don't happen very often, if at all. In fact, men who take on work that's traditionally performed by women often find that they're singled out for special praise and attention because they've broken through such a big barrier. It's also worth remembering that, as traditionally 'male' jobs shrink in number, men who are unwilling to consider 'women's work' could well end up with no work at all.

As the labour market evolves, we may also need to change our idea of what we understand by a career. The notion that we can start at the bottom and steadily work our way to the top is rapidly becoming a fantasy for all but a few. Becoming multi-skilled, through experience of work in a wide variety of fields, could enable us to take advantage of many more opportunities.

Whether we can successfully change direction – even when we're sure we want to – depends on many factors. Age, commitments (perhaps to a mortgage or children, or both), **201** skills, experience and qualifications can all affect our options. We may have to accept that change will be gradual – perhaps starting with some part-time retraining – or even delayed until our children leave home. But once we know that we really do want to do things differently, we won't be fully satisfied unless we at least attempt to make it happen.

## alternatives

With two-thirds of workers saying that they'd like to work shorter hours, there are other changes we could make to improve our working life as well as giving us the opportunity to follow other interests, spend more time with our children or retrain for another job. Here are some possibilities to think about:

- **Job sharing:** *an arrangement where two people share one full-time job between them. They share the work, pay, holidays and benefits. Usually, everything is split 50/50, but other divisions are possible. Job sharing is becoming increasingly popular, particularly in the public and voluntary sectors.*
- **Part-time work:** *this is the most common way of working fewer hours, although part-time jobs tend to be concentrated in areas of work traditionally done by women and are often low paid with limited job security. At the moment, just 10 per cent of men work part time compared with 45 per cent of women.*

- **Flexible working hours ('flexitime'):** *outside 'core hours', when an employee must be at work, staff are allowed to spread an agreed number of hours over the week.*
- **Time off in lieu:** *instead of getting paid for overtime, the employee has the option of taking time off work instead.*
- **Career break schemes:** *staff are allowed to take an agreed period of time off work (without pay), but still have a guaranteed job.*
- **Working from home:** *with new technology, it's easier for many employees to work completely or partly from home while remaining in close contact with their employer.*
- **Alternative organizational structures:** *many men's struggle to succeed is reinforced by the fact that most workplaces are set up in a hierarchical and competitive way. Finding work in less hierarchical or even collective/cooperative organizations can be a way of stepping off the greasy pole. These organizations will often be small and in the voluntary sector.*
- **Self-employment:** *as more and more organizations contract their workforce, an increasing number of ex-employees are trying this option. Indeed, the typical organization of the not too distant future may well be one with a small core of staff employing a much larger number of self-employed people on short-term contracts. The new self-employed will become so-called 'portfolio' workers, each doing a variety of work for a range of organizations. Self-employment provides much greater independence – there's more choice over when and how* **203**

*work is done – but the insecurity can also encourage (or necessitate) overwork and lead to high stress levels. The self-employed carry their own overheads – they have to buy their own equipment, perhaps rent an office and make provision for sick and holiday pay – so it can be harder to generate a reasonable income. They also miss out on many of the social aspects of work. However self-employment is on the increase and many find 'being their own boss' a much more satisfying way of working.*

- **Voluntary work:** *often men think the only work that really counts is what they get paid for. However, many have found voluntary work immensely satisfying. As well as being something men can feel committed to, it can give us new skills and experience. It can also be a way into a new kind of job for the future.*

A survey of men by the organization New Ways to Work found changing to more flexible working patterns increased their motivation and energy as well as enabling them to spend more time with their family and friends, be involved in community activities and follow leisure interests. This proved positive for both the men and their employers. Other research has also suggested that men who spend more time with their children become better at time management, listening and negotiating, as well as more adaptable. Even though employers may be initially reluctant to allow their male staff to work more flexibly, and might even doubt their commitment to the job, it could well be in their long-term interests to do so.

# fit for work

The real man may not worry about his health in the workplace, but he's more likely to be the one off with backache, cuts and bruises or concussion after a brick's fallen on his unprotected head. The healthy workplace is not simply accident-free, however. It's one where the chairs and desks are ergonomically designed, where the lighting and ventilation are properly adjusted, where the computers are not used for more than 50 minutes at a time and where background noise is kept to a minimum. The healthy workplace is also one where staff can take their full lunch-hours, all their holidays and are not expected to work excessive overtime.

Employers are also now beginning to realize the importance of a physically fit and healthy workforce. Some 'blue-chip' companies pay for their staff to join commercial fitness clubs, while others provide gym facilities on site. Even if our company doesn't help out, we can take steps to help ourselves by creating the time for exercise. Research from the USA shows that participation in an exercise programme cuts absenteeism, creates a more positive mental attitude and boosts morale. A study by the space agency NASA also found that staff who exercise become much more productive – they tend to work at full efficiency all day while other workers' efficiency decreases by 50 per cent in the final two hours of the working day. The whole idea of getting fit for work may well fill us with horror. It could remind us of those PE lessons at school we so desperately wanted to bunk off, or pictures of Japanese workers being led through their stretches before being led into the **205** factory. However, it's a fact as hard as a bodybuilder's biceps that the physically fit employee is not only more efficient but also happier.

It's vital for our mental health that we also find effective ways of dealing with stress. Stress isn't just caused by work of course – ill health or relationship problems could just as easily be implicated – but work is often the part of our life where we experience it most. Technically, stress is the state of arousal with which our bodies respond when threatened. Our bodies would naturally deal with these challenges by preparing to fight or run away; but most modern men do neither. Instead, we continue to live with the stress which, over time, can lead to harmful physical and mental consequences. Common stress-related symptoms include headaches, migraines, muscular tension, coughs, abdominal pain, diarrhoea, indigestion, tiredness, allergies, insomnia, an inability to concentrate, lowered sexual desire, impotence and baldness. Stress is known to affect the body's immune function and lead to increased susceptibility to disease; some doctors suspect that stress may even play a role in potentially life-threatening illnesses such as coronary heart disease and cancer.

Of course, both men and women suffer from stress, but there are some specific ways in which men may be susceptible. Because we're encouraged to achieve and compete, many of us try to push ourselves far beyond the point where we feel secure or comfortable. At the same time, however, our emotional repression makes it harder to deal with the feelings. Many of us, therefore, try to deal with stress by denying it.

Alternatively, we try to block it out by overeating, overdrinking or smoking. These strategies can often, in turn, lead to higher levels of stress. What could be more useful is to find ways of dealing with stress creatively. If we can identify when we're feeling stressed and what's causing it, we can learn how to make positive changes. In part, these could include practical things which increase our ability to relax and cope. Of course, it may also be that the stress is being caused by a situation from which we might be better off removing ourselves, such as an unsatisfactory job or relationship.

Even if we can't free ourselves from a stressful situation, there are a number of simple ways we can still go about reducing our anxiety. Think about trying the following:

- *Identify if anything specific is causing you stress and devise strategies to overcome it. For instance, if your computer keeps crashing, ask for better software and/or training. If you're constantly disturbed by colleagues discussing their social arrangements for the weekend by your desk, ask them to move elsewhere.*
- *Learn how to manage your time better. Try making lists of tasks to do – including their deadlines – and rank them in order of priority.*
- *Don't take on more work than you can handle. Learn to say 'no' with confidence. You may feel that you're admitting failure, but it's better to do what you take on well than to do a lot more badly. As you gain experience, it's likely that you'll be able to take on more.*

- *Take regular breaks – try to get out of the workplace at lunch time and don't stare at a VDU all day. Break up your daily work routine as much as you can.*
- *Look after your health. Try to avoid dealing with work problems by increased drinking or smoking. Watch the caffeine too – overdosing can definitely make you jumpy.*
- *Take your full holiday entitlement. Ending the leave year with 20 untaken days may impress your employers for a time, but they're less likely to be inspired if you then have to take three weeks off sick to recuperate.*
- *Try to learn mental and physical relaxation techniques. Breathing exercises can be a good place to start. When we're feeling stressed, we may start breathing rapidly and more shallowly; in extreme cases, this can lead to hyperventilation. Deep breathing exercises can help draw air deep into the lungs and aid relaxation. Try closing your eyes and, as you take deep breaths, just listen to – and feel – the air going in through your nose and out through your mouth. Meditation can also be useful. This isn't just for Buddhist monks in the deepest Himalayas. Anyone can learn how to meditate and to direct thoughts away from life's problems. To try meditating, find a quiet place, sit or lie down and spend ten minutes or so just focusing on your breathing. Close your eyes and notice how the air goes in and out. If your mind wanders – and it probably will, especially at first – don't worry, just gently draw it back to your breathing. At the end, take a minute to notice your surroundings and stretch before*

you get active again. Meditation has been shown to lower your blood pressure, pulse and breathing rate. Exercise, yoga and massage can be other good ways of dealing with pressure. And think about getting a pet – seriously. Stroking a cat, or even staring at a tank of fish, can really reduce stress levels – it's not for nothing that pet owners are at less risk from heart disease.

- Try to keep a sense of humour and to have a good laugh at least once a day. Like exercise, laughter releases endorphins, the body's own natural painkillers, and makes you feel better. Sharing a joke can also improve the work atmosphere and boost motivation.

- Talk about your work anxieties with a friend or partner. Try not to be one of those men who comes home sitting on a volcano but can only say 'fine' when asked how his day was.

- Develop a 'rounded' lifestyle outside work. Cultivate your other interests and make time to see friends. If you've got children, at the very least, try to be home before it's time for the bedtime stories and keep your weekends free to spend with your family.

- Think about joining a trade union, if you haven't done so already. It can help with advice and support if you're facing difficulties. Ultimately, if your employer won't take action to reduce your stress levels, you may need help to make it happen. In any event, just being part of an organization that's there to represent your interests can help you feel less isolated and more powerful at work. **209**

# doleful

Imagine that you've worked in the same place for five years. Your boss is happy with your work and you're at last earning decent money – that BMW convertible now looks like a real possibility and your girlfriend's looking forward to a holiday in the Seychelles. Your career looks set to rise and rise and, although you work very hard, you find the job creative and stimulating. But then disaster strikes. An unwise investment by a colleague in the Far East hits the confidence of clients, millions are lost, cuts have to be made. By the time you've caught your breath, you're standing in the dole queue, your girlfriend's run off with your best friend and you've even had to sell your clapped out Mini Metro to pay the gas bill.

The big 'U' – unemployment. It's unexciting, undesirable and definitely unmanly. Real men don't lose their jobs – they may die at the end of the film, but at least they don't have to suffer the indignity of signing on. In reality, of course, millions of men do. We're living in an era of large-scale, long-term unemployment. Even middle-class men, previously largely untouched by the consequences of recession, have become all too aware of the implications of losing a job. If our employer has 'enhanced our leisure opportunities' (corporate-speak for being thrown on the scrap heap), we're probably more likely to blame ourselves for not working hard enough than the government or the World Bank for mismanaging the economy. Our feelings are likely to include despair, resignation and passivity; our physical health may well suffer; and our relation-

ships with partners and friends could also be affected.

There's no question, unemployment stinks. However, in one sense at least, it does provide an opportunity. Despite all the financial constraints, despite the blow to our self-confidence and self-esteem, there is the option of trying new things – possibilities include looking after the children, voluntary work, political activity, an exercise programme, hobbies or further education. Men who are able to develop new interests and a different purpose in life are known to adjust better to unemployment than those who are overwhelmed with feelings of shame and failure.

## the times they are a changing

It used to be easy for men – full employment was virtually guaranteed and a sense of masculinity and power could be derived from work. Men still want their masculinity confirmed through work, but that's no longer so easily achieved. As well as the risk of unemployment, men face job insecurity through the short-term contract, increased competition from women and the decline of the traditional heavy industries with their demand for hard physical labour. Employers now require staff with more 'feminine' skills such as teamwork and communication. If we're working in a fast-food restaurant, the boss wants us to be friendly and pleasant to the customers, not to terrify them by pulsating our pectorals. And with women now making up about half the working population, men can no longer see themselves as the sole family breadwinner.

These changes can threaten men but they also create new possibilities for us to review our working lives. Perhaps more than any of the other issues discussed in this book, work offers a powerful incentive for us to look at ourselves and to consider the opportunities for personal development. For a start, simply to survive, the modern worker has to find ways of accepting the reality of change and of learning to adapt to it. Trying to stand against it is to behave like King Canute – at the very least, our feet will get wet; at worst, we'll end up completely submerged.

Embracing personal development means much more than acquiring new and specific skills, such as learning a new computer programme, double-entry book-keeping or how to conduct an interview. Many employees are now expected to learn quickly and flexibly, reconcile conflicting demands, discover new solutions and, perhaps above all, communicate effectively. These are personal skills that can't be learnt from a book or a flip chart. Rather, staff need to be able to discover, and then put to use, their own latent strengths and to broaden the range of their potential responses to new challenges. This involves identifying, and overcoming, the habitual and perhaps rigid or ineffective ways in which we've traditionally handled problems. Outdated attitudes to working relationships – including an inability to delegate and an authoritarian approach to management – are common limitations shared by many of us.

Being able to work effectively with women – both as colleagues and as people above and below us in the hierarchy – is particularly important. Although many men, especially if they're older or working in traditionally male-dominated professions, still treat female staff as if they belong to an almost alien species, it's a simple fact that more and more of us will be working alongside women whatever job we do. If we try to ignore them, freeze them out, unfairly criticize their contribution or spend our time sexually harassing them, then ultimately we'll be the ones who lose out. We'll be judged incompetent, inefficient, uncooperative, oppressive and dispensable.

Whatever he does, the real man at work exhibits a potent combination of strength, bravery and power. He doesn't worry if his job takes up too much time, he's not bothered about whether his job is unsafe and he certainly doesn't lie awake at night wondering if he might prefer working with children or animals. For most of us, of course, it's not quite that simple. If we're in work, we probably worry about our job security, our prospects, whether our work is good or appreciated enough, whether we're working too hard or maybe not hard enough, or even whether we're doing the right job in the first place. If we're unemployed, we might worry about ever getting another job. Employed or not, we could be aware of a yawning gap between where we think we should be – successful, rich, powerful – and where we feel we actually are. Any of us might therefore find it useful to take a step back from work and reflect on whether it's really meeting our needs.

213

If we're honest, does our work satisfy us? Is it really what we want to be doing? Are the physical and emotional demands exhausting or invigorating? Would more flexible working arrangements be better? And what about our work at home? Do we believe we're doing a fair amount of housework or would our relationship, if we have one, be strengthened by more active involvement? Given the amount of time we spend at work, getting our relationship to it right could be one of the most important steps we can take towards becoming a complete man.

# fathering:
# the nurturing man

## daddy

For many of us, happy memories of our father may be few and far between. Maybe we remember the excitement when he came home from a work trip or a sense of closeness when he taught us how to kick a ball, but beyond that, our father was often the parent we never knew. During the day, he was probably out at work, and in the evenings he may well have been either too tired to play with us or too keen to have some time for himself. The time we did spend with our dad may well have lacked the intimacy we had with our mum. Few boys kiss and cuddle their father as freely as they do their mother. Our dad may have been the person we'd avoid when we'd done something wrong, rather than the person to whom we'd tell our secrets or problems. For many of us, even now, dad remains a shadowy figure, uneasily lurking in the background at family gatherings or slumped in an armchair watching television. Given that the majority of one-parent families are mother-only, some of us may not have known our father at all.

It's argued – predominantly by American mythopoetic

writers – that the distance between a boy and his father can chronically arrest a male's psychological development. Because fathers are emotionally 'unavailable' or absent, boys lack a positive role model to guide them towards male adulthood. It's suggested that, consequently, many men have problems 'growing up' and developing a sense of themselves as responsible, independent adults. On the outside they may have beards, beer guts or balding pates, but inside they still feel as insecure and uncertain as spotty teenagers. And, when they do act mature and manly, it's not because they feel confident about being an adult, but because they're desperately trying to cover up the fact that, actually, they don't know what they're supposed to be doing. It's also suggested that this lack of a paternal role model forces men to look towards media images of masculinity as a way of filling the gap.

Men who have started to look at their feelings towards their father often discover a deep well of grief, or anger, for the paternal love and intimacy they never had. Consequently, they've realized that, deep down, they've been longing for their father to 'return' and give them all the fathering they've missed out on. So long as they're doing this, however, it's hard for them to take full responsibility for their own lives.

If this is happening – and we may not know it is until we start to examine the relationship – it's important to explore this sense of dependency on our father. Accepting that our dad will never provide for us the love we've always yearned for can be very painful. But it's often only through grieving, and accepting the pain, that we can emerge as an adult in our own right.

216

We might need to grieve for all the hours we expectantly waited for him to return; the instances when he put us down or pushed us away; the times when he ignored us, scolded us, beat us or even sexually abused us.

Until we explore these feelings, it may be very difficult to relate to our father on an adult-to-adult level. If we still long for him to parent us, or if we're angry with the way he treated us as a boy, these emotions may stand in the way of a closer relationship with him in adult life. We may well not even want to take the risk because of a deep-seated fear of rejection – after all, it happened before. If we start to examine our feelings, however, we may both deal with the grief and realize why he behaved as he did. It may be that he was straitjacketed into the masculine role just as we are – probably even more so, given how much more rigid gender roles were when he was growing up. Moreover, there may well have been many positive things our dad did give us and these will become increasingly apparent as we accept our negative feelings towards him.

Looking at the relationship with our father might also help us to see how we have adopted some of his behavioural and emotional characteristics – not expressing feelings, being emotionally distant or using aggression instead of negotiating. It can facilitate our relationship with our own children, too. If we realize the pain of his absence, then we'll know how important it is to be around when our sons and daughters are growing up. We may also discover that it's important for us to be emotionally close to our children. But it's difficult to get in touch with our nurturing side when we are still expecting **217** someone else to come along and nurture us. The more we develop our sense of ourself as an adult, the more we can contribute to our own child's upbringing.

## getting stuck in

Just 30 years ago, you'd almost never see a man pushing a pram or changing a nappy. If a baby cried or needed feeding, it would automatically be passed to mummy. If a child was ill, mother would be nurse. Fathers might read a bedtime story or play cricket with their sons in the back garden, but their involvement with children was generally minimal. Their role in the family was to bring home the bacon, not to cook it and feed it to junior. Men are now beginning to be more active fathers but, in most relationships, women are still doing the bulk of the childcare. Men tend to choose the bits that are pleasurable – such as going to the playground on a Sunday morning – rather than the daily grind of washing, feeding and comforting. We may now be pushing the pushchair, but most of us are doing it with just one hand.

A number of obstacles still stand between men and active fathering. For a start, although hunky Gillette men can be seen hugging babies in television adverts, the inner Arnie thinks looking after babies is about as effeminate as playing with dolls. After all, most real men don't have children – James Bond might spend a lot of time copulating but it's certainly not in order to reproduce – and those who do are too busy killing terrorists to be around mopping up their offspring's vomit. So even if we enjoy being with children, it certainly does less for our masculine image than being at work, playing football or hanging out with our mates down the pub. Most of us still see childcare as women's work.

We may also feel that, when it comes to children, we're all fingers and thumbs, awkwardly standing around wondering what to do and feeling out of our depth. Most of us are not brought up with much information on how to father. We probably didn't learn much from our dad and, although we may have played with a toy Action Man, we may well have spent most of our time banging its head against a wall. Women's magazines are often crammed full of tips about motherhood, while men's magazines provide either endless pictures of naked women or information about which mobile phone to use – reading them will make us none the wiser about the simple realities of parenthood. Television's pretty useless too. There are not many realistic images of fathers, just endless gruesome adverts and sitcoms where men are figures of fun whose parenting skills extend little beyond burning the fish fingers while demolishing the kitchen. And the chances are that, at school, information about fathering was equally lacking, limited to finding out how rabbits copulate or, if you were lucky, how to use a condom.

Even where men are keen to step into the world of child-rearing, the organization of our work can be a major impediment. It can be difficult to get time off to accompany our partners to antenatal classes or check-ups. Even when the baby is born, we may have to take leave from work in order to attend **219** the birth and spend time at home in the difficult following week or two. British men have no legal right to paternity leave whereas, of course, most women are entitled to an extended period of paid maternity leave. The fact that men usually earn more than their partners can also trap us into the breadwinner role since, from a financial point of view, it can seem more logical for men to continue working while their partner takes time off work for childcare.

What can also prevent men getting involved is the idea that women are somehow natural mothers – as much a myth as the idea that men are natural warriors. Men can be just as good parents as women; the only thing we can't do is breast-feed. American psychological research into the origins of nurturing behaviour suggests that, as infants, boys and girls don't differ in their knowledge of infant characteristics or readiness to care for an infant themselves. Men who decide to get involved with childcare have been found able to learn nurturing skills quite quickly. With experience, men are just as good as women at interpreting baby noises like sucking, burping, coughing and crying. Psychologists have also discovered that even male rats – not normally among nature's best carers – develop nurturing behaviour when confined with newborn rat pups.

We have much to gain by choosing to be active fathers besides striking a blow for women's equality. Fatherhood can put us more in touch with our emotions and make us more empathetic, nurturing and caring as well as less aggressive and selfish. Intimacy and involvement with children can also help us to rediscover an ability to have fun, play and muck around and help us to break through the serious reserve with which many of us surround our lives. In these ways, childcare can encourage men to develop those important qualities at the 'feminine' end of the masculine/feminine spectrum.

If we do leave the childcare up to our partners, we'll also be perpetuating the traditional system of sex roles. If our children see their mother playing a caring role and their father a going-out-and-earning one, then it's quite likely they'll believe that this is how they should behave as well. If, on the other hand, they see both parents taking an active role in childcare, they're clearly more likely to grow up with a sense of equality between the sexes.

## to father or not to father?

Fatherhood doesn't start when the baby pops out in the delivery room. It begins the moment the decision to have a baby is taken. And that means we can consider our role from the very beginning, even before the condoms are thrown away or the pills flushed down the toilet. With more and more women now putting their careers first and deciding to remain childless (20 per cent of all women born in the 1970s and 1980s are expected to have no children), it may even be worthwhile reflecting on whether we want children before we decide to 'settle down' in a long-term relationship.

It can be very hard for us to think about having children, however. It's common for women, who know that they are living with the pressure of a 'biological clock', to have more of a sense of urgency about children and to take the initiative. Although some men are keener to have children than their partners – and, traditionally, men have seen producing progeny as an expression of their masculine virility – we often feel we can wait another few years, perhaps until we've got that all important promotion at work and are more financially secure. In a Gallup survey of 540 men aged 20–45, 35 per cent said that they had children mainly because their partner wanted them.

If we're in a long-term relationship, it's important to be fully involved in making the decision to have (or not to have) children. This is partly because our detachment from the issue can leave our partners feeling irritated, or even very alone, but it's mainly because the decision is probably one of the most important, life-changing decisions we'll ever make. It will affect us much more than deciding to buy a house or taking a new job and, perhaps, more than getting married or divorced. So it's a decision that requires at least as much thought, discussion and planning.

A good place to start thinking about whether we want a child or not is to make a list of the pros and cons of having a baby. Here are some questions we might find useful to ask ourselves and to talk about with our partner:

- *Do you enjoy spending time with children? (If you don't know, you may want to spend some time with the children of friends or relatives to find out.)*
- *Is your relationship strong enough to survive the inevitable strains of childcare?*

- *Can you afford a baby?*
- *Do you have the time, or are you willing to make the time, to devote to a child?*
- *Are you having a baby to try to revive a dying relationship?*
- *Could you organize your work to enable you to be the father you want to be?*
- *Would you be having children out of a sense of duty or obligation (perhaps to your partner or your parents)?*
- *Would you be having children because you want to leave something permanent after you've gone?*
- *Will you resent compromising your life for your child? Are you prepared for someone else to be the focus of your life, putting their needs before your own, for the next 18 years?*
- *Do you want children because you're scared of being alone or uncared for in your old age?*
- *How would having, or not having, children affect your sense of masculinity?*

If we do decide to become a dad, it's worth thinking about getting into shape. It's now known that the better the father's health, the greater the chances of conception. Our sperm are more likely to be of good quality if we cut down on smoking and drinking. We could try, too, to keep our testes cool (so no tight jeans) and avoid unsafe contact with dangerous substances at work such as lead, heavy metals, solvents, pesticides and radiation. And we're more likely to be able to **223** cope with the rigours of our partner's pregnancy and childbirth – not to mention childcare – if we're fit and healthy. So it's worth taking regular exercise and eating plenty of fresh fruit and vegetables.

Of course, some men will impregnate a partner by accident. With the exception of sterilization, no form of contraception is 100 per cent effective. In this case, we may need to decide whether our relationship is a viable one as well as whether we want to have the child. Faced with these tough questions, many men simply panic and disappear, either literally or emotionally. We may urge our partner to have an abortion before any other option has been discussed and before she has had a chance to talk about her feelings. While it's important for us not to feel coerced into a course of action that doesn't feel right – and which we could well later resent and rebel against – it's also true that we share a responsibility for deciding what to do.

## a bun in the oven

For many men, pregnancy can be nine months of confusion, excitement and sometimes even terror. It's unknown territory (at least for the first time around) and we may feel we know too little about what's going on or what we're supposed to do. We may feel displaced from a central role in our partner's life, our place having been usurped by the developing foetus. We may even feel intensely jealous or even resentful of the as yet unborn baby.

This sense of rejection can be reinforced by our partner's lack of interest in, or physical inability to have, sex at times before (and after) the birth. During the first trimester (three months) of pregnancy, many women experience morning sickness and exhaustion and lose interest in sex. In the second trimester, however, many women report heightened sexuality both in terms of desire and physical response. Sexual activity usually drops off again in the final trimester. It can be a challenge for those of us who equate sex and closeness with penetration to develop other forms of sexual expression, tenderness and intimacy with our partners. Other men believe, wrongly, that intercourse can harm the foetus and may end up avoiding the very kind of physical contact actually desired by their partner. It's worth knowing that our penis can't poke our baby in the eye and a little hand can't reach down and grab the end of our member.

Even though we and our partner may have made a positive decision to have a baby, the reality of pregnancy may bring up a lot of new uncertainties for both of us. We may dread how it will dramatically change our life and resent having to give up our dreams of flying to Paris for the weekend or taking that trekking holiday in the Himalayas. In Gallup's survey of 450 men, one third said that they regretted not being able to do things on the spur of the moment once they became fathers and one fifth regretted having less money to spend as they pleased.

During pregnancy, expectant fathers are expected to be sturdy oaks, providing support for their partners. We've **225** probably all seen the movie scene where the man, when told his wife is pregnant, immediately asks if she's alright, makes her lie down and rest before starting to prepare the supper for the first time in five years. Pregnant women may often feel unwell, scared and vulnerable and do need the help and support of their partners. At the same time, however, there's usually little recognition of the fact that we may need some support too – not necessarily from our partner (she may already have enough to cope with), but from our friends or relatives. We might find it useful to talk about our fears of being trapped by encroaching domesticity, worries about the forthcoming birth or feelings of becoming more marginal to our partner's life.

Some men change their physical appearance during pregnancy, perhaps growing a beard or putting on weight. Others may experience problems such as toothache, decreased appetite, vomiting, constipation, insomnia or irritability – all symptoms similar to those experienced by pregnant women. In some cultures, men even retire to their beds and act out labour pains. This phenomenon, known as the 'couvade' syndrome, may well be a reflection of men's anxiety or – in a less generous interpretation – an attempt by men to attract attention at a time when they feel physically and emotionally neglected. However, recent Italian research comparing men with pregnant partners to an equal number of 'non-pregnant' men came to the surprising conclusion that couvade symptoms actually occurred more frequently in the non-pregnant group.

226  Men can also lessen their anxieties by becoming more

informed about pregnancy and childbirth. This could involve expectant fathers talking to other parents and reading books as well as attending antenatal classes with their partners. We could even try wearing the so-called 'empathy belly', a strap-on pregnancy simulator weighing 28 pounds and simulating 20 symptoms of pregnancy (including foetal movement and pressure on the bladder). One definite advantage of attending classes is the opportunity to make contact with other men going through similar experiences. In fact, it could be worth considering meeting with other men who have pregnant partners – either individually or in groups – and to talk, share concerns and find ways of supporting each other.

But pregnancy is not just a time for the man to sit around, feeling anxious and waiting for something to happen. There are many useful things we can do during pregnancy:

- *Most importantly, perhaps, you can try to be available to your partner. Many men, particularly as the pregnancy advances, find all sorts of reasons to stay at work late, take on new commitments or start new hobbies. It's as if they're trying to cram as many final 'childless man' experiences as possible into the few months they feel they've got left. This behaviour, while understandable, is unlikely to be appreciated by your partner.*
- *Ask your partner what support she needs. She may spend time, particularly during the first three months, feeling unwell. She may not be able to perform many of the household tasks she previously did and you may*

> want to take on some or all of these responsibilities.
> She may also welcome a regular massage or other
> physically relaxing attention.
> - *Nest build. Prepare your home for the baby: finish off
>   any necessary DIY, prepare your baby's space. Be
>   involved in buying (or getting from relatives or friends)
>   any clothes or equipment you may need.*
> - *Help your partner to prepare her birth plan. This is for
>   the midwives and doctors to follow during childbirth. In
>   it, your partner can specify in what circumstances she
>   wants drugs to be used and what position she would
>   prefer to give birth in.*

A man whose partner has become pregnant may of course
lose the child, either through choice (by an abortion) or by
accident (because of a miscarriage or stillbirth). Such a loss is
inevitably traumatic, certainly to the woman but also to her
partner. When a child is lost, the mother understandably
becomes the focus of attention and support. The father will
be expected (and expect himself) to be part of that support,
but this can mean that his own feelings of anger and grief
remain unacknowledged. These feelings may be even
stronger where a partner decides on an abortion against the
man's wishes or without consulting him. A relationship can
be profoundly affected by the loss of a child. Each partner
may come to blame the other for what happened and sex
may become problematic if there's a fear that the situation
will recur. Sometimes, women who have experienced a

miscarriage or stillbirth try to become pregnant again quickly even though their partner is reluctant. All these issues need to be talked about, possibly with the help of a therapist.

## out it comes

The majority of men (about 90 per cent) now choose to be present at the birth of their children. Childbirth is, for many, an extraordinary, moving, powerful event and many men attending a birth experience an ecstatic peak of emotion either at the moment of birth or within a few hours of it. A Royal College of Midwives survey of over 400 men found that over 60 per cent thought being present in the delivery room was a 'wonderful' experience.

Our presence can help our partner too. One study found that the partners of men who attended labour and birth reported that they felt less pain, received less medication and had more positive feelings about the whole experience than women whose partner had not been present. Most men attending a birth felt that they'd made a useful contribution: a survey of 730 men at a London hospital found that 84 per cent thought that they'd helped to sustain their partner's morale. About one fifth of men also cut the umbilical cord.

However, another study found that all the men who were at the birth suffered enormous stress and that the practical assistance they offered was limited; indeed, they spent most of the time trying to hide their feelings and worrying about their usefulness. The Royal College of Midwives survey also found that 30 per cent of men were scared by the experience and 3 per cent were actually sick. It seems the actual effectiveness of a man's contribution is directly related to the amount of his antenatal preparation – so the more we know and have practised before the birth, the more relaxed and useful we can be in the delivery room.

If you find yourself in the delivery room but are not quite sure what you're supposed to be doing, try:

- *Letting your partner know she's not alone in a strange environment with strange people.*
- *Helping your partner to relax by massaging her neck, shoulders and back.*
- *Reminding her of how to breathe.*
- *Encouraging her through her contractions.*
- *Accepting her anger – many women feel furious during delivery, with the midwives, the doctors, the baby and even you.*
- *Acting as a mediator between your partner and medical staff and, if necessary, standing up to the doctors and midwives on your partner's behalf.*
- *Welcoming your baby into the world as soon as possible after the birth. The baby will probably be scared too – after all, they've just come out of a warm, dark and comfortable nest into a bright, colder and strange new world – so a loving face won't go amiss. Often, the mother is too exhausted to have much to*

*do with the baby (or she may require medical*
*treatment, such as the stitching up of a caesarean*
*section or an episiotomy – when the tissue between*
*the vagina and the anus has been cut to help delivery).*

It is important for each of us (together with our partner) to decide for ourselves whether our presence at the birth will be useful. It may now be common but it's certainly not compulsory. If, for example, we feel faint at the sight of blood or have feelings of guilt about being the cause of our partner's pain, then we may be more of a hindrance than a help. Also, some women might prefer to have a female friend or relative present, or feel too exposed or vulnerable during childbirth and not want their partners to see them. Some men commit themselves to being there only for the first stage, not the actual delivery. Then, when the time comes, they and their partner can decide if they'll stay or go.

## fathercare

Mike, a 38-year-old actor describes the home birth of his daughter Carol as 'The most fantastic experience I've ever had in my whole life.' When the midwife turned up, she saw Mike sitting in the corner:

'You're not sitting over there,' she said. 'You come over here and roll your sleeves up.' She even encouraged me to cut the umbilical cord. Jane, my partner, fell asleep an hour **231** or two after giving birth although Carol was wide awake, so I had to carry her around the room on my shoulder all night. I remember she sucked my earlobe.

However, Mike did not find that he was immediately attached and being a father took time to grow on him:

I didn't do very much childcare until my first daughter was about a year old. It wasn't something that felt natural to me. My father was very traditional. He went to work at 7.30 every morning and came home at 6. He had his dinner and sat there with his slippers on. My mother was a traditional mother who stayed at home, did the housework and looked after the family. But Jane pushed me to be more involved. At first, to be quite honest, I resented that. I felt henpecked. I think most men feel that if they're being cajoled into doing house work, they're losing out on their manly rights. But now I'm all for it. Doing childcare actually reinforced my own sense of individuality. I did what I wanted to do.

Some of Mike's early ideas about childcare were slightly unrealistic:

I thought you could just stick a baby in a play pen with some toys and carry on doing your own thing for a few hours. Then you'd give them lunch and put them back. But I soon realized that was impossible; babies need your full attention. So I've had to learn and develop a lot of new skills. Childcare has made me more considerate, gentle, caring, tender – things that are seen as 'womanly' attributes. I've also realized that to look after children you have to be very fit and have a lot of stamina. It's a 12 hours a day, seven days a week job with no pay packet and nobody saying thank you. But I see it all as an investment for the future.

As Mike has found, parenting can be enjoyable, but it can also be tough. There's a lot of hard work involved and a great deal of sleep can be lost. Many parents end up walking around like zombies, exhausted but unable to rest. Some men also no longer find their partners attractive once they've become mothers. Women can resent their partner's lack of involvement in childcare and feel isolated and depressed by the daily, and tiring, routine. With the end of the extended family, many parents can find themselves isolated as they cope with the unknown. It's not surprising that relationships frequently come under great strain during a child's first few years; indeed, more marriages break up in the 18 months after childbirth than at any other time.

Postnatal depression affects up to 15 per cent of women and it's recently been found that some men suffer from it too. It's often triggered in men by their partner's depression, although it can also affect those whose partners are not depressed. Often the key issues are men's inability to cope with their partner's feelings and their resentment about the **233** attention devoted to their partners by other people. Men can also exacerbate their partner's depression if they feel marginalized by the new baby and so unable to support their partner. This underlines the importance of men getting support at this time, whether they're depressed or not.

Unemployment's pretty lousy, but it can give us opportunities to spend time with our children. If we're in work, we can take annual leave – or, if we're lucky, paternity leave – when our children are born, so we're around for at least one or two weeks full time. That's not much, but it can help. Other possibilities could include negotiating a longer period of unpaid leave (if we can afford it) or a temporary or permanent period of part-time work. It might also be possible to make use of flexitime to work nine-day fortnights or to cope with particularly difficult periods (when our child's ill, for example).

It's also worth considering more radical approaches to our work, perhaps even giving it up altogether to allow our partner to return to work. After all, she may earn more than us, she might enjoy her job more, or we might enjoy looking after children more than her. Alternatively, we could agree that we'll take a year or two off work followed by her doing the same. Perhaps we could both work part time so that our child has full-time care. Or we could both work full time and use a childminder or a nanny. Even if we end up working in a conventional way, there are still opportunities to have good contact with our child. It's a myth, for instance, that babies have to go to bed early, and we may be able to spend time

234 with our child when we get back from work. At the

weekends, we might want to take complete responsibility.

Fathers often have a special interest in their sons. We may feel a closer affinity to them or that we can share special time with them, perhaps doing things our father did (or never did) with us. Many of us place unrealistic expectations on our sons and hope that they will achieve whatever has eluded us. We may be particularly concerned that they grow up to be 'proper' men: independent, strong and, above all, heterosexual. We may also have feelings of jealousy and competition with them: in the first five years or so, we may feel resentful of our boy's closeness with his mother and, when he becomes a young adult, jealous of his opportunities, including his sexual relationships.

Men's relationships with daughters can be equally complex. We may be less interested in them because they are not male and see it as natural for them to have a primary relationship with their mother. This neglect can be confusing for girls and even affect their future relationships with men – for example, they may end up in a fruitless search for relationships with men which seem to offer the kind of fathering they never had. However, we may also feel overprotective of our daughters, especially when they begin to mature sexually, and this may lead to resentment or encourage a daughter to feel weak and vulnerable.

One issue that may come up with daughters – and possibly with sons – is that of sexual attraction. As a child matures, a father may find himself becoming sexually aroused by his child. For the father, this can be a very confusing and distress- **235** ing experience. Needless to say, men should never, ever act on such feelings and initiate sexual contact of any kind with children. Apart from the legal consequences of such behaviour, sexual abuse is undoubtedly damaging to the children involved. However, being honest about and acknowledging these feelings – and seeking support – is a more positive approach than denying we have them. This is difficult, of course, given the taboos about discussing incest and child abuse in our culture.

It's increasingly common these days for men to enter into a relationship with a woman who already has children and, not surprisingly, a complex mixture of feelings can result. We may resent her children, feeling that we want a relationship with her rather than her offspring; we may feel jealous if the children have a better relationship with their biological father than with us; we may feel that we're supposed to take on the role of disciplinarian in the new family. But being a good step-parent means acknowledging that we can't have a relationship with a mother without having a relationship with her children, and accepting that building a relationship with the children may not be easy and may take a long time. It's also advisable for us to avoid getting into the role of laying down the law, as that will almost certainly alienate us from the children.

Talking to friends, especially other dads, about this issue and other aspects of fatherhood, can be immensely useful. A father's group might be even better – such a group could meet for two or three hours once a month and also be available for advice or support over the telephone at other times. Although vast numbers of men are fathers, it's rarely an experience men share. The expectation we have of ourselves and each other is that we just get on with it, that somehow we automatically know how to be and what to do. Just as men won't ask for directions when they're lost in the street, so we don't ask for help when we haven't a clue what to do with our children. If we can overcome these inhibitions, we'd probably feel less isolated and much more competent as dads.

## where's daddy gone?

With at least one in three new marriages now ending in divorce, and cohabitation arrangements even less stable, many fathers are ending up living apart from their children. Obviously, relationship breakdowns can cause great pain for all concerned, including the children, but fathers often face particular problems.

Even if we've agreed to our children living with our ex-partner, we may still feel as if they've somehow been removed from us and that the access arrangements are too restrictive. This can happen even though, as in most cases, the children's mother believes that they should have some relationship with their father. Feelings of guilt at abandoning the children, of rejection by them, or of loss and powerlessness may well be expressed through blaming our former partner. This is especially likely to happen in cases where the courts have intervened and decided that the children can live with their mother and specified the extent of our contact. Issues of financial **237** support for the children may also have created problems.

Sometimes it's easier for us to believe 'It's all her fault' than acknowledge our feelings directly. Our pain may even lead us to feel that it would be easier to reject the children and never see them or their mother again. Maintaining a good relationship with children in this situation is far from easy. Because the children will probably still have a close relationship with their mother, we need to find effective ways of dealing with any feelings of bitterness towards her. If we don't, then we could well end up pushing our sons and daughters to take sides. This is of no use to them or, ultimately, to us. By remaining hostile to an ex-partner, arranging contact and discussing the children's upbringing becomes almost impossible. On the other hand, putting negative feelings about our ex to one side can bring to the surface all we regret about the loss of the relationship.

It can also be hard for men to maintain close and loving relationships with children who they may not see for long periods of time, especially if they end up living some distance away. When we do see our children, especially if they are babies, we may feel we lack the necessary caring skills. There may not be a woman around to do the kinds of things that we're not used to, such as changing nappies or dealing with tears. It's also worth remembering that the children may be angry with us for what will look to them like abandonment. We may have to work hard to regain their love and trust.

There are no easy answers to these problems, but even after

we have separated from our partner, relationship counselling or family conciliation services might help to sort out the extent of our contact with our children. There are also many ways in which we can keep in touch with children we no longer live with. Sending photos we've taken or tapes or videos we've recorded, writing regularly and (of course) using the phone can all help. We can also support their interests and hobbies by sending them materials. We could ask them to send us stuff too, perhaps copies of their schoolwork. It's important to show that we are taking an interest in their lives.

In cases where fathers keep custody of the children (or where their partners die), single-parent men can face particular problems. Childcare support tends to be run for and by women, and a single dad may find himself excluded from parenting networks. If he leaves his work to look after the children, he may well feel isolated and trapped. For men in this position, asking for support can be hard at first, but it may be the only way out. Contacting a community group for parents or looking for support from friends and relatives can be positive first steps.

Any man looking through his scrapbook of male heroes is unlikely to find many who have much to do with children. They may end up protecting or saving children – as Arnie does in *Terminator 2* and *Commando* – but mostly they're too busy fighting the enemy to play with Meccano or macramé. Most men looking to their own past for paternal role models are likely to find a man who may not have been away fighting but was more than likely to have been absent **239** working. Despite all the talk of the 'new father', it's still all too easy for men to fall into the traditional role of being distant and uninvolved with their children. But is this what men really want? Do we want to have the same relationship with our children that our father had with us? Can we do better? Being an active father raises so many questions about our role as men that perhaps it's easier for us to try to forget them. However, those who have tried to become more involved – by thinking seriously about whether they want to have children, by being supportive during pregnancy, by being at the birth and by maximizing their opportunities for spending time with their children – find it a positive and rewarding experience. Parenting is never easy or free of stress, but it can bring the complete man in touch with a range of emotions – unconditional love, wanting to care and nurture, joy – that he's seldom, if ever, been aware of.

# in conclusion:
# the complete man

We've come a long way since discussing the origins of the inner Arnie in the prehistoric tribe sitting round its cave. We've looked at how, if we want to, we can extend our emotional literacy, improve the quality of relationships, become more sensuous and intimate during sex, less prone to violence, healthier and more in tune with our bodies, more fulfilled at work and, finally, more involved with children. Taken together, this amounts to a comprehensive personal development programme for any man who wants to explore, and perhaps change, his life.

We live in an exciting and challenging time for men. The opportunities for personal transformation have never been greater. The traditional roles of men and women are breaking down – just as it's increasingly accepted that women can play an equal role at work, so it's easier for men to express a wider range of emotions and to be more active fathers. Counselling and therapy have become widely accepted by many men and women as valid means of re-evaluating personal identity. The changing nature of work – especially growing job insecurity **241**

– is also increasing many people's desire to look for ways of enriching their lives, both within and beyond the workplace. There now exists a greater understanding of masculinity – it's no longer just seen as an inevitable biological by-product of having a penis but much more as a socially constructed set of attitudes and behaviours which can be changed – and it's widely acknowledged that the traditional, real man has outlived his usefulness.

But it's still not easy. The inner Arnie is firmly lodged in our heads, kept there both by our own fears about exorcizing him as well as social attitudes. We've all been brought up to believe that we have to behave in certain ways to be respected and loved and so, consciously or not, we're all searching for a way to be the 'ideal man'. 'If only I could be like Arnie,' we think, 'then I'd be happy. I'd have lots of money, lots of girlfriends and lots of respect.' So we wonder what will happen to us if we start to change? Will our partner and our friends still like us? Will people make fun of us? Will we be humiliated or attacked? Will people think we're gay if we start to show our feelings? What will our lifestyle be like if we change our priorities? What job will we do? Will we end up living in a commune, wearing purple trousers and eating muesli five times a day? These are just some of the questions that will almost inevitably concern any man contemplating changing the way he lives. No matter how much we may dislike many aspects of our current life, making big changes almost always feels more frightening than just soldiering

242 on. We've got so used to listening to our inner Arnie, it's hard

to contemplate ignoring his advice. However, as with any stale relationship, there comes a time when we have to make some changes. It's not about throwing away the inner Arnie, but understanding him, standing back from him, and making choices.

So how do we start? This book contains many practical suggestions, from improving listening skills to developing assertiveness to managing anger. And all these can help. But perhaps the biggest single step any man can take is to start talking. Not only about the usual subjects – sport, cars and politics – but about all the private stuff we normally keep well hidden. Once we open up about our lives – to begin to tell it as it really is – we can start to understand much more about ourselves. And as we talk about our childhood, our work, our relationships, our sexual experiences, our body, our fears, our hopes, our dreams, our mum, our dad, our schooldays, so we'll begin to get more in touch with our feelings.

Who can we talk to? Perhaps a trusted friend, a partner or a therapist. Or maybe even a men's group. That may sound wacky, maybe a bit frightening, but a group can be an excellent place to share ourselves with others who, simply by virtue of being male, can empathize with much of our experience. Moreover, hearing other men talk honestly about their lives can help us to understand more about ourselves and enable us to see how other men also struggle with the constraints imposed by the inner Arnie. And if we're not yet ready to talk to anyone, we can still try writing. Keeping a diary, or describing key events from our past, can be an **243** excellent first step. Our journal can stay hidden at the bottom of the wardrobe – nobody else ever has to see it (or even know it's there).

It's much easier to open up if we remember some basic ground rules. It can help if we always talk in the first person ('I feel') rather than saying 'one' or 'you'. It can be better to avoid intellectualizing about our emotions – in other words, not to distance ourselves from our feelings by thinking about them as if they belong to someone else. We can try not always to distract ourselves from our feelings by some sort of displacement activity – perhaps watching television or cleaning the car – and to avoid taking drugs to numb ourselves out. We can also practise letting other people know how we feel, even if it's about only small things at first. So if our partner irritates us by always wanting sex five times a night, we can try telling her. It's vital for us to learn that the world will not end whenever we reveal an emotion.

We may well find it hardest to admit our vulnerabilities, our weaknesses and our feelings of simply not knowing what to do. Appearing defenceless and indecisive certainly will not win us many votes at the Mr Real Man of the Year Award, but owning up to these feelings is still one of the most important steps we can take. No longer pretending that we've got all the answers can not only make it easier for us to relate to others, it can also enable us to get the help or support we need to lead a better life. It may mean that we'll talk to our partner or a friend when we're feeling low, see a doctor when we're sick or tell

244 our boss when we can't cope at work.

Although many of us might feel scared about beginning to express ourselves, once we start it can actually feel an immense relief. Because we've become so used to repressing our feelings, many of us can feel as if we're sitting on a volcano of thoughts and emotions. Once we begin to open up, we can be almost unstoppable. It's often said that men are essentially cold, unemotional and unfeeling or that it's easier to talk to a stone than have a decent conversation with a man. But this reflects how men have been brought up rather than how we really are. Once we're given the opportunity to talk, many of us will seize it eagerly and enthusiastically.

Finally, it's important to remember that none of us has to become any particular type of man, no matter whether it's a real man, a new man or a wild man. Swapping our inner Arnie for an 'inner Woody Allen' or an 'inner anyone else' would simply exchange one set of constraints with another. What's important is for each of us to have access to a complete range of human possibilities – from one end of the masculine/feminine spectrum to the other – and to choose what's most appropriate for each situation. Trying to be a real man is like always ordering chicken and chips whether we're at the local cafe, a Chinese restaurant, a pizzeria or the London Ritz. Being a complete man isn't about always ordering quiche instead; it's about choosing whatever takes our fancy at the time.

Once we start to make changes, it's unlikely that we'll ever want to go back to how we were. Whatever the difficulties of becoming a different kind of man, few of those who have **245** started on the journey regret their decision. Once we've tried dim sum, poached salmon, asparagus tips or a Four Seasons pizza, we're unlikely to want to return to an exclusive diet of chicken and chips; becoming a complete man opens up the possibility of a more enjoyable, exciting and fulfilling life.

# further reading

## magazines

*Achilles Heel: The Radical Men's Magazine*
22 Cliff Villas
Camden Square
London NW1 9AT
01273 734 079
Britain's only 'alternative' men's magazine, exploring topics such as sex, relationships, work, emotions and fathering from a humanistic, pro-feminist perspective. Essential reading.

*Working With Men*
320 Commercial Way
London SE15 1QN
0171 732 9409
For professionals who work with men on issues of violence, sexism, sexual abuse and masculinity.

## books

John Archer and Barbara Lloyd, *Sex and Gender* (Cambridge University Press, 1986). Psychology of sex differences. **247**

Robert Bly, *Iron John: A Book About Men* (Element Books, 1994). Core mythopoetic text.

Nikki Bradford, *Men's Health Matters: The Complete A-Z of Male Health* (Vermilion, 1995).

Sarah Brewer, *The Complete Book of Men's Health* (Thorsons, 1995).

Nigel Edley and Margaret Wetherall, *Men in Perspective: Practice, Power and Identity* (Prentice Harvester, 1995). Academic overview.

Nancy Friday, *Men in Love* (Hutchinson, 1993). Male sexual fantasies.

Mitch Golant and Susan Golant, *Finding Time for Fathering* (Fawcett Columbine, 1992).

Germaine Greer, *The Female Eunuch* (Flamingo, 1971). Feminist bible.

Shere Hite, *The Hite Report on Male Sexuality* (Random Australia, 1990).

Robert Johnson, *He: Understanding Masculine Psychology* (HarperPerennial, 1990). Jungian analysis.

Sam Keen, *Fire in the Belly: On Being a Man* (Piatkus, 1991). Personal mythopoetic account.

Christopher Kilmartin, *The Masculine Self* (Macmillan, 1994). Authoritative sourcebook for 'men's studies'.

Michael Kimmel (ed.), *Men Confront Pornography* (Meridian, 1991). Essays for and against pornography.

Michael Kimmel and Michael A. Messner (eds.), *Men's Lives* (Macmillan, 1989). A book of readings.

Mike Lew, *Victims no Longer: Men Recovering From Incest and Other Sexual Child Abuse* (Cedar, 1993).

Sarah Litvinoff, *The Relate Guide to Better Relationships* (Vermilion, 1991).

Sarah Litvinoff, *The Relate Guide to Sex in Loving Relationships* (Vermilion, 1992).

Andy Metcalf and Martin Humphries (eds.), *The Sexuality of Men* (Pluto Press, 1985). Academic but accessible.

Richard Meth and Robert Pasick, *Men in Therapy: The Challenge of Change* (Mind, 1994).

New Ways to Work, *Balanced Lives: Changing Work Patterns for Men* (New Ways to Work, 1995). Alternatives to the daily grind.

Richard Olivier, *Shadows of a Stone Heart* (Pan, 1995). Personal mythopoetic account

Angela Phillips, *The Trouble with Boys* (Pandora, 1993). An accessible look at the way boys are brought up.

Yvonne Roberts, *Mad About Women: Can There Ever be Fair Play Between the Sexes* (Virago, 1992). Accessible British feminist analysis.

John Rowan, *The Horned God: Feminism and Men as Wounding and Healing* (Routledge, 1987). History of the British men's movement and male archetypes.

James Ryan (ed.), *Sinews of the Heart: A Book of Men's Writings* (Five Leaves Press, 1995). Personal accounts of male lives.

Lynne Segal, *Slow Motion: Changing Masculinities, Changing Men* (Virago, 1990). Detailed analysis of men's political and personal development.

Victor Seidler (ed.), *The Achilles Heel Reader: Men, Sexual Politics, and Socialism* (Routledge, 1991). Collection of early articles (available from Achilles Heel address, see page 247).

Mark Simpson, *Male Impersonators* (Cassell, 1994). Cultural analysis of straight men's fears of homosexuality.

John Stoltenberg, *Refusing to be a Man: Essays on Sex and Justice* (Meridian, 1989). Pornography, sex, and power; strongly pro-feminist.

Bernard Zilbergeld, *Men and Sex: A Guide to Sexual Fulfilment* (HarperCollins, 1983).

# useful organizations

chapter 2. **emotions:** the feeling man

## *men's groups*

Information about men's groups (and conferences, workshops and other events) is available from:

*Achilles Heel*
  See page 247 for contact details.

Men's Databank
  c/o Derek Shiel
  25 Randolph Crescent
  London W9 1DP
  0171 286 1173

Men for Change Network
  c/o Flat 6
  75 Dartmouth Park Hill
  London NW5 1JD
  0171 482 5953
  (Enclose a stamped addressed envelope.)

## counselling and psychotherapy

British Association for Counselling
  1 Regent Place
  Rugby CV21 2PJ
  01788 578 328

Re-evaluation Co-counselling
  Contact: Graham Elliott
  01727 760 067

The Samaritans
  10 The Grove
  Slough
  Berkshire SL1 1QP
  0345 909 090

United Kingdom Council of Psychotherapists (UKCP)
  167–169 Great Portland Street
  London W1N 5FB
  0171 436 3002

## chapter 3. **relationships:** the intimate man

## sexism

National Alliance of Women's Organisations (NAWO)
  PO Box 257
  Twickenham TW1 4XG
  0181 891 1419

## *homophobia*

London Lesbian and Gay Switchboard
  PO Box 7324
  London N1 9QS
  0171 837 7324

Stonewall
  16 Clerkenwell Close
  London EC1R 0AA
  0171 336 8860
  Lesbian and gay campaigning organization.

## *relationship counselling*

Relate (National Office)
  Herbert Gray College
  Little Church Street
  Rugby CV21 3AP
  01788 573 241

## chapter 4. **sex:** the sensual man

## *sex addictions*

Sex Addicts Anonymous
  BCM Box 1457
  London WC1N 3XX
  0171 402 7278

## *Impotence*

The Impotence Association
  0181 767 7791


## *sex therapy*

British Association for Sexual and Marital Therapy
  PO Box 62
  Sheffield S10 3TS


## pornography

Men and Porn Group
  PO Box 3677
  London N15 6SQ
  0181 690 7512


## *contraception*

The Family Planning Association
  2–12 Pentonville Road
  London N1 9FP
  0171 837 5432


## *HIV and AIDS*

National AIDS Helpline
  PO Box 5000
  Glasgow G12 9JQ
  0800 567 123 (minicom) 0800 521 361

Terrence Higgins Trust
  52–54 Gray's Inn Road
  London WC1X 8JU
  (helpline) 0171 242 1010 (daily noon–10pm)
  (administration and advice centre) 0171 831 0330

## chapter 5. **violence:** the peaceful man

*domestic violence*

CHANGE
  University of Stirling
  Stirling
  Scotland FK9 4LA
  01786 471 215
  Contact for local organizations.

Domestic Violence Intervention Project (DVIP)
  PO Box 2838
  London W6 9ZE
  0181 563 7983

Nottingham AGENDA
  First Floor
  202 Mansfield Road
  Nottingham NG1 3HX
  0115 969 1475

## *male sexual abuse*

Survivors
  PO Box 2470
  London W2 1NW
  (helpline) 0171 833 3737

## chapter 6. **bodies:** the healthy man

### *general*

Men's Health Network And Resource Centre
  North Derbyshire Health Promotion Service
  Scarsdale
  Newbold Road
  Chesterfield S41 7PF
  01246 231 255 ext. 4280/6

The Men's Health Helpline
  0181 995 4448

### *testicular cancer*

Mind Over Matter (testicular cancer support group)
  14 Blighmont Crescent
  Millbrook
  Southampton SO15 8RH
  01703 775 611

## infertility

ISSUE: The National Fertility Association
  509 Aldridge Road
  Great Barr
  Birmingham B44 8NA
  0121 344 4414

## prostate problems

Prostate Help Association
  Langworth
  Lincoln LN3 5DF
  (For initial information sheet send two first-class stamps.)

# chapter 7. **work:** the fulfilled man

New Ways to Work
  309 Upper Street
  London N1 2TY
  0171 226 4026

The Network for a New Men's Leadership
  45 Nutgrove Avenue
  Bristol BS3 4QF
  0117 940 7254

# chapter 8. **fathering:** the nurturing man

Parent Network
  44–46 Caversham Road
  London NW5 2DS
  0171 485 8535

# international resources

## australia

Men's Contact and Resource Centre
  PO Box 8036 Hindley Street
  Adelaide SA 5000
  0061 8223 1110

*XY: Men, Sex, Politics*
  PO Box 26
  Ainslie ACT 2602
  0061 6248 5215
  Australia's male-positive, pro-feminist and gay-affirmative men's magazine.

*The Men's Resource Book*
  PO Box 41
  Hughes
  ACT 2605
  0061 6285 2707
  This book, available from the above address, gives details of individuals and organizations providing information, support and services for men in Australia and New Zealand.

## canada

Men's Network for Change
  c/o Ken Fisher
  133 avenue des Plages
  Pontiac (Luskville)
  QC JOX 2G0
  (001) 819 455 9295

White Ribbon Campaign
  220 Yonge Street, Suite 104
  Toronto
  Ontario M5B 2H1
  (001) 416 596 1513
  Men's anti-violence organization.

## united states of america

The Men's Center
  Warner Gateway
  Suite 130, 21860 Burbank Boulevard
  Woodland Hills
  Los Angeles
  California 91367
  (001) 818 348 9302

National Organization for Men Against Sexism (NOMAS)
  Suite 300, 54 Mint Street
  San Francisco
  CA 94103
  (001) 412 731 2234

# index